W9-CEE-190
MARBORO

NOVA YOGA
The Yoga of the Imagination

NovaYoga

The Yoga of the Imagination

GEORGE FRANCIS BARTH

Mason & Lipscomb PUBLISHERS NEW YORK

ISBN: 0-88405-014-9

LIBRARY OF CONGRESS CATALOG CARD NUMBER: 73-87433

PRINTED IN THE UNITED STATES OF AMERICA

FIRST PRINTING

DESIGNED BY ANDOR BRAUN

to EDNA, *whose fondness for the beach, the edge of the sea, and me, led to the formulation of this book*

CONTENTS

PART TWO

NovaYoga in Action—*Case Histories*

Foreword

I first became acquainted with the NovaYoga Technique of Self-Realization when my daughter brought me a manual of applied self-image psychology* asking for my opinion of its validity. As with so many young people today, she was interested in learning a viable procedure of relaxation.

I found the manual most interesting. Because I have always considered it important that a practicing physician be interested in the study of different and contributory sources of knowledge that could improve the quality of the medical service provided his patients, I am an avid reader.

Treatment of the total person is the goal of psychosomatic medicine. This includes the employment of whatever ancillary procedures are available to relieve the tensions of psychological conflicts and distortions of self-image which can aggravate bodily ailments.

Hypnosis, a long-recognized therapeutic procedure, and yoga meditative techniques are being increasingly investigated in an effort to achieve expanded and better functioning of both mental and physical processes. The research work of Dr. Joseph Kamiya in the field of electroencephalography has received wide publicity at the professional level and in the popular press. His studies of yogic and Zen Buddhist meditators in the attainment of

---

* *How to Be the Person You Want to Be,* published by The Nova-Yoga Center, Inc., New York, New York, 1968.

the alpha rhythm, and the biofeedback training this makes possible, have provided a scientific basis for such procedures as the NovaYoga mantra meditation for the release of tensions.

If this book, which is an amplification of the original manual my daughter brought me, offered nothing more than training in NovaYoga mantra meditation, it would still be a boon to many thousands of persons from all walks of life by relieving their tensions.

However, NovaYoga, as the name suggests, is a new school of yoga – a yoga of the imagination. This is immensely interesting, because training in the control and development of the imagination can enable one to reap huge rewards, not only in relieving tensions but in biofeedback procedures that can help one to implement psychosomatic procedures. NovaYoga is specifically oriented toward training the individual to overcome his conditioned inhibitions and toward helping him to develop the personality pattern of the person he wants to be.

NovaYoga is actually an eclectic method which draws upon the works of many psychologists and many schools of psychological thought. Similiarly, it follows techniques drawn from hathayoga, mantrayoga, and layayoga.

I have witnessed the good results of this remarkable autogenic training method. Not only does it offer relief from all tensions, but it offers a way to recondition negative imagery. As a physician, I consider this kind of positive self-image training of great help in the treatment of many psychosomatic disorders. It is especially valuable in treating some depressive states and self-depreciation. Besides its practicality I find the book considerably inspiring. I endorse it enthusiastically.

ATTILIO MORPURGO, M.D.

Sag Harbor, N.Y.

And Krishna explained the meaning of Yoga to Arjuna . . . "When the mind, intellect, and self are under control, freed from restless desire, a man becomes one with the spirit within.

A candle does not flicker in a place where no winds blow; so it is with a yogi who controls his mind, intellect, and self, being absorbed in the spirit within.

When the restlessness of the mind, intellect, and self is stilled through practice of Yoga, the yogi, by the grace of the spirit within himself, finds fulfillment.

*Then he knows the joy eternal which is beyond the pale of the senses which his reason cannot grasp. He abides in this reality and moves not therefrom. He has found the treasure above all others.**

There is nothing higher than this. He who has achieved this shall not be moved by the greatest sorrow.†

This is the real meaning of Yoga – a deliverance from contact with pain and sorrow."‡

---

* the pearl of great price (*NovaYoga mantra meditation*)
† release of all tension (*NovaYoga Meditative Relaxation*)
‡ the ultimate state of tranquility (*NovaYoga Center of Tranquility*)

PART ONE

THE NOVAYOGA TECHNIQUE OF SELF-REALIZATION

Chapter 1

The Yoga of the Imagination

THERE ARE MANY variant schools of yoga. The school with which we in the West are probably most familiar is Hathayoga – the *yoga of force* – which emphasizes the physical means of attaining self-realization. Another school is Mantrayoga, the *yoga of spells*. Layayoga is the *yoga of dissolution* and Bhaktiyoga is the *yoga of religious love*. NovaYoga, as the name suggests, is a new school of yoga. It is a psychic yoga for the *now* generation – the *yoga of imagination.*

In his book, *The Living Brain,* Dr. W. Grey Walter explores the modern science of electroencephalography – the area of research that has sprung into the forefront of interest with such terms as "alpha rhythm," "theta rhythm," and "biofeedback." Dr. Walter points out that the brain of homo sapiens differs from the brute brain in only one (vital) aspect: *imaginative faculty.* No other animal brain has this faculty.

Soon after Pavlov, the Russian physiologist and psychologist, succeeded in demonstrating the conditioned reflex in 1904, his experiments inspired another researcher, Walter Hunter of Chicago, to create a similar series of experiments. However, Hunter demonstrated the *lack of the imaginative faculty* through the inability of his test animals to remember a visual signal (in this case a light over one of three doors) for more than a very few minutes. Not one of the dogs in his experiments was able to visualize the light after it was extinguished. The possession of an imagination would have enabled the dog to choose the correct door and thus earn its reward of food.

What Is the Imaginative Faculty?

In most psychology books, in discussing fantasy or creativity, *imagination* is usually defined as the ability to create an image. But according to Dr. Walter, the imaginative faculty is the outstanding characteristic of the human brain!

Yoga teaches that the world of your true reality lies within – not without – you. The psychologist teaches that you perceive reality by means of sensory experiences with your consciousness. It is because of your faculty of imagination, however, that your consciousness is able to use your sensory experience. It does this by creating that imagery with which the brain performs the prodigious feats of memory, reason, association, and discrimination – which form your stream of consciousness and without which there would be no reality as we know it.

By use of reason and discrimination, exploring memory and association, the imaginative faculty is able to create new images through combination of images previously experienced. The only other mind which man recognizes as having this capability is that we call "god." Indeed, the concept of God is one of the grandest achievements of the human imagination. No other animal brain has the imaginative capacity to gaze into the heavens and think of the mind of God and then turn this gaze inward and echo the words of St. Paul: "The Kingdom of God lies within. . . ."

But persons differ in visual imagination, as William James pointed out when he was discussing Sir Francis Galton's *Inquiries into Human Faculty.* In this famous questionnaire, Galton developed the knowledge that one's imagination can be visual, auditory, gustatory, olfactory, tactual, or motor-inspired. In other words, the imaginative faculty employs the perceptions. Most of us are stimulated by our sense of sight. However, like Beethoven, who composed and inwardly heard his symphonies, there are many whose imaginations are stimulated by their sense of hearing. Others still are stimulated by their sense of taste, smell, touch, or by images created through muscular sensation.

You may be assured, even though you claim you cannot see or visualize clearly, that you have an imaginative faculty of one or the other types, and it doesn't matter which.

Your mind uses your imaginative faculty in remembering everything. It creates images which become the symbols of ideas. It can do more. Your mind uses images retained from past experiences to create *new* images that do not exist. It can project into the future with images of its own creation.

It is because of this unique ability that man has been able to influence nature and rise from the primeval swamp to walk on the moon. It can be said, therefore, that the power man has gained over nature and himself is due to his ability to control his imagination.

Everything you do, whether deliberate or autonomic, is done first by your imaginative faculty. This is subliminal, below the level of your conscious mind. If you are anxious about some upcoming event and therefore tense, you may be sure that in your imagination you have *visualized* your response to this future event negatively, thereby creating anxiety. On the other hand, if you are confident about the outcome, you are free of tension because in your imagination you have created a positive, self-confident success image.

NovaYoga may be described as self-image psychology structured on a framework of yoga. The basic principle of NovaYoga was expounded some three thousand years ago when Solomon said, "As a man thinketh in his heart – so is he."

Your Life Goal Is Happiness

As H. G. Wells learned in researching his monumental *Outline of History,* every one of the millions of human beings on this planet is, in his own way, seeking happiness.

Happiness is *your* goal, as it is mine. But what is one man's meat (happiness) is another man's poison (unhappiness). How, then, can we define happiness in a way that will be meaningful to both of us?

Happiness is an emotional state, a kind of euphoria resulting from a sense of physical and mental well-being. As you will learn from your study of NovaYoga, this emotional state is attained as you develop your ability to cope successfully with your environment, and as you become emotionally mature.

There is probably no one who is entirely without *some* personality problem. This problem may be unrecognized as such, although it is evidenced by such feelings as excessive shyness, self-consciousness, self-depreciation, or feelings of inferiority, insecurity, or rejection. The resulting symptoms can be obesity, insomnia, excessive smoking, or worse still, drugs – and always tension.

The young person of today, the product of a permissive upbringing, may be groping to find himself. He finds the mores of the establishmentarian generation bewildering and confusing. Brought up without sensible *guidelines* taught with understanding and intelligent discipline, much of the Now generation is blindly seeking a goal, an objective – actually self-realization.

To many, reality is totally devoid of the values which provided inspiration and motivation to an older generation. Without such motivation, reality can become fearsome and adjustment so difficult that normal maturing experiences only serve to reinforce the negative self-images of the unfulfilled personality.

The Goal of NovaYoga

NovaYoga is an eclectic system of autogenic training based on tested and proven techniques which begin with A] *self-hypnosis*, to learn the fundamentals of relaxation and experience the Alpha rhythm; B] *astral projection*, to condition oneself to experience a deeper, altered state of consciousness; C] *Pavlovian reconditioning*, to establish a new, positive self-image of the person one wants to be; D] *mantra meditation*, following seeding suggestions which germinate, eventually to become that "pearl of great price," the new personality of the person you want to be.

The techniques and disciplines employed follow the procedures of suggestion psychology and of hathayoga, layayoga, and mantrayoga. The *focus*, however, is not on spiritual enlightenment but the attainment of emotional maturity, and thereby, the self-realization of your innate talents, capabilities, and capacities.

The ultimate goal of total *serenity* is attained through the reconditioning of your negative self-image to the positive success image of the person you want to be.

Electroencephalographic Research

All training in meditation – whether in the classic form of mantrayoga or with the aid of instrumentation such as an electroencephalograph (EEG) or in NovaYoga mantra meditation – has as its objective the training to achieve, at will, that altered state of consciousness which in mantrayoga is known as *samadhi,* in the use of an electroencephalograph is known as the alpha and/or theta rhythm, and in NovaYoga is known as *the center of tranquility.* In each instance the *altered state of consciousness* attained connotes total absence of *tension.*

Dr. Joseph Kamiya has received publicity because of his early research into the sleep state by means of electroencephalography. He learned that subjects experience total freedom from tension when they reach the alpha rhythm. Later work, using instrumentation which would control lights to monitor it, has shown that with practice a person is able to reach the alpha rhythm at will. Later still, when Dr. Kamiya moved to the Langly Porter Neuropsychiatric Institute of San Francisco, he began work with yoga and Zen Buddhist meditators. He quickly discovered that their meditative states produced not only alpha but theta rhythms. With these meditators, the electroencephalograph functioned merely as a monitor; it wasn't necessary as a training instrument.

Other researchers on sleep have confirmed Dr. Kamiya's work. Sleep psychologist David Foulkes identifies the alpha rhythm with the *hypnagogic state* of light sleep. Whatever imagery is present is semi-voluntary, as in revery when the mind is passive, no longer concentrating. This is the state of consciousness that is attained in NovaYoga meditative relaxation and in mantra meditation.

There are four brain wave patterns being researched:

beta – 14 to 30 cycles per second are emitted in the waking state;
delta – 0.5 to 3.5 cps, the deepest sleep state, unconscious;
alpha – 8 to 12 cps, the light, hypnagogic sleep state, and
theta – 4 to 7 cps, the deep, hypnagogic sleep state which releases your creativity and your imagination.

The Differences Between Mantrayoga, Instrument Training, and NovaYoga

A popular form of mantrayoga is known as *transcendental meditation* (T.M.), which was taught to the Beatles and became widespread when the Maharishi Mahesh Yogi established centers in the United States to teach his form of mantra meditation. In Hindu, a mantra is supposedly a magic word or expression which, when repeated over and over, eventually brings the subject into that state of consciousness which frees him of tension and develops serenity and peace of mind.

A similar sense, or feeling, of euphoria is attained when one experiences the alpha rhythm with the use of an EEG or an instrument known as an electroencephalophone (EEP).

The NovaYoga student soons trains himself to attain serenity, peace of mind – that sense of euphoria when the mind and body are freed of tension. However, the fundamental difference between the three techniques is that T.M. and EEG training proceed without regard to one's hangups. Whereas the feeling of relaxation may be learned, the basic reason for the need of such training (that is, one's hangups) is not overcome. NovaYoga training, therefore, may take a little longer, but when it is completed, a person not only attains that wonderful sense of serenity, but an altered personality pattern that can result only from emotional maturing – to become the person one wants to be.

You Never Outgrow Your Need for Love

Don't you feel wonderful when someone dear to you embraces you tightly and says, "You're wonderful. I love you!"? It doesn't matter if you're six months, six years, or sixty years old – you *always* need love. You need love especially when you are born, and you need it as you grow through childhood and adolescence.

Loving care and guidance with intelligent discipline is the first principle of NovaYoga. The importance of this principle was never more dramatically demonstrated than when a grandmother of 62 came to me for training in the relief of tension. With tears streaming down her cheeks she cried, "Mother didn't love me!" She had lived a whole lifetime of rejection, frustration, inhibition and tension!

Love is the most powerful, the most transcendent emotion you will ever experience in the whole of your lifetime. Without it your life is empty, bleak, barren. With it your entire life experience is a joy and your whole being feels fulfilled. The sky is bluer, the sun is brighter, all your senses are sharpened; in a way, they become psychedelic. You then develop that glorious feeling of self-esteem. For only if you are loved and are capable of returning love can you truly have self-esteem.

Without such self-esteem you may experience feelings of inferiority, inadequacy, unworthiness. From such feelings can stem a galaxy of personality-maladjustment symptoms. Not the least – and probably the most common – is the problem of the *underachiever*, so inhibited by negative feelings that he cannot make full use of his innate talents, capacities, and capabilities. With self-esteem he is motivated to make full use of his talents, capacities, and capabilities. He has the drive to aspire to a goal, the ambition to become the person he wants to be.

Love, especially the tactile demonstration of love (hugging, kissing, petting), is most important to your ego/id development soon after you are born. Actually, you experience two births. The first is when the obstetrician pats your behind and you sound your first cry. This is the *physiological* birth. Your second birth occurs when the obstetrician hands you to your mother and she holds you lovingly against her breast and hugs you. This is your *psychological* birth. Children who do not experience this psychological birth can become autistic, reject reality. With them normal communication is blocked.

No one knows what goes on in the infant's mind during the process of birth. But it can be assumed that the experience is traumatic. No one really wants to be born. As an embryo you were quite satisfied with your environment. You were warm, well fed, perfectly comfortable within the fluid environment of your mother's womb. That the birth experience is indeed traumatic was demonstrated by a young woman, a somnambule, who was referred to me by her medical doctor. During the first training session (which you will learn in a later chapter) she eagerly slipped back into her childhood to recall her early experiences; experiences that may have caused her tension. She found them, starting when she was nine years old, when her mother made her responsible for the care of her three smaller sisters.

She was only nine and deeply resented the role her mother had given her. She felt rejected and angry. Her anger made her ill, and she eventually developed the diabetes for which her doctor was treating her.

Finding her such a responsive subject, I urged her to slip back further in her recall in *meditative relaxation.*

She slipped all the way back to her birth, recalling the anguish, the fear of being forced through a dark tunnel and out into glaring light. "The noise," she exclaimed holding her ears, "the noise!" The glaring light threatened her. The rough handling stimulated panic. It wasn't until she felt herself being held, hugged, that she felt a lessening of the fright. She felt more secure, less frightened of this new, awesome environment into which she had been thrust so violently. She was born psychologically.

This is a single, isolated instance of total age-regression on the part of an unusually responsive subject who was somnambulistic. She was a deeply emotional person and felt that she had been abandoned by her mother when she was told, in effect, that she could no longer be a child but had to assume a mother's responsibility.

What is this emotion we call love? Why is it such a powerful factor in our lives? At the primitive level it provides the drive within every human being, indeed every living thing, that strives to insure the perpetuation of the species. Freud characterized it as an element of the libido, but it is far more than a sex instinct. It encompasses the primal urge to live – and self-preservation is the first law of life. It is of such transcendence that we describe it as the first characteristic of God.

In NovaYoga love is characterized as the basic principle of life. One aspect of this active principle is the powerful drive toward *identity,* the power that impels the individual to self-realization. In a child this force is self-seeking, selfish, demanding of sensual satisfaction. Nature has designed it to be so, because if the newly born of any species lacks this powerful urge, survival is threatened.

The NovaYoga postulate is that you are *now* the result of your earliest conditioning experiences, that the personality pattern you developed is due to your emotional response to *love experiences* (providing a feeling of security) or the lack of love experiences (creating a feeling of insecurity).

It would be a fairly simple matter if every child's response to his early life experiences was always the same. Such responses, however, are infinitely varied. Whereas in almost identical circumstances, one child will respond to a life experience with feelings of rejection (and subsequently develop feelings of inferiority), another will become excessively aggressive as he quickly learns how to demand and force attention (love experience) from his mother.

Why does one child passively accept apparent loss of love experience, while another child makes aggressive demands until he receives the love experience he craves? The theory to which NovaYoga subscribes is *genetical inheritance.* The particular combination of chromosomes that carry the genes establishes your hereditary characteristics. This has been observed in the actions of fraternal twins where one develops passive characteristics and the other becomes aggressive.

This is not to suggest that either one or the other pattern is to be preferred. Early conditioning with respect to ego-satisfying love experiences (or lack of them) can cause traumatic responses in the aggressive as well as the passive child. The resulting adult personality patterns can differ in that the aggressive child becomes *compulsively* demanding (not only of others but of himself), while the passive child accepts a self-image of being unworthy (and develops feelings of inferiority). The result, in the first instance, could be *over*achieving, while in the second, *under*achieving. Either one poses a personality problem.

Obviously the ideal situation is when a child inherits normal, well-balanced genes, receives intelligent care and attention, with ample love and discipline, during the formative years from parents who are emotionally mature and who therefore can provide an environment for the child that is loving and free of stress-producing experiences.

Since we cannot choose the character of our genetical inheritance we can at least hope for emotionally mature parents. Indeed, we have a right to demand that not only will *our* parents be emotionally mature, but that *all* parents be capable of providing the proper environment in which to bring up their children.

In our society certain restrictions are placed on the individual so he won't pose a threat to others. For example, if you wish to drive a car, you are required to learn how to handle it. You are required to learn the rules and regulations concerning the movement of your vehicle in traffic. Then you are required to learn to control your emotions, overcome fear, and demonstrate your competency by passing a driving test. Then and only then are you permitted to drive the car.

Compare this significant restriction to your total freedom in a relatively insignificant role (driving a car) with the almost total lack of restriction in another role that has infinitely greater implications of potential danger to our society — the role of marriage. In our "free" society anyone who is pronounced free of venereal disease and is of legal age can by paying a small fee secure a marriage license and legally bear children — who may become emotionally crippled, burdens to themselves and to society.

There is no test of the competency of prospective parents to provide the proper mature environment in which their children can develop into emotionally secure individuals free of the emotional problems and personality hangups that so frequently prevent such children from attaining personal fulfillment — and happiness. If we have a sick society it is because we allow this continuing pollution within our society in much the same way that we allow the pollution of our air, water, and environment in general. Is it too much to ask that the prospective mother and father *first* pursue some course of study (as is required for a car license) in the psychodynamics of marriage and child-rearing *after* undergoing an examination of competency (a determination, based on accepted psychological standards, of some degree of emotional maturity of both individuals) and, if indicated, be required to undergo training which can lead to such maturing *before* being issued a license to bear children?

NovaYoga abhors regimentation and advocates a totally free society composed of emotionally mature individuals. The objective of NovaYoga training is to free yourself of hangups that inhibit and prevent you from fully developing your talents, capabilities, and capacities, in short, to attain emotional maturity.

The Three Stages Toward Emotional Maturity

Freud held that there are six phases of ego development: the *oral* phase approximates the first year; the *anal* phase approximates the next two years; the *phallic* phase until the fourth year, blending into the *oedipal* phase in the fifth year; next is the *latency* period, which continues until approximately the eleventh year; and finally the *puberty* phase approximately until the fourteenth year.

Psychologist Erik Erikson has refined this concept to include eight stages that carry one into old age, when one attains either integrity or despair. His postulates, for each stage, are persuasive. However, NovaYoga adopts the position that the human brain is indeed a computer that is being programmed during every moment of one's life experience. These life experiences, which involve a change of pattern (that is, a change in one's environment, physical as well as emotional) can be many more than Erickson's eight.

How many such stages until one attains true emotional maturity varies with the individual. But first, let us understand what *maturity* implies. NovaYoga holds that you attain emotional maturity in terms of your ability to adjust (happily) to your environment. Obviously this does not mean that because you are an adult, you are also mature. How many times have you observed an adult person react to a given situation (or to a transaction) as a child would? Transactional analysis, as described by Eric Berne in *Games People Play*, lays particular stress on the child life experience as a continuing influence in one's adult life.

NovaYoga postulates that there are three basic periods in your life experience, with the third stage continuing throughout the whole of your life. The periods are:

The AFFECTIVE PERIOD – the first year of your life, when you are capable of responding to your environment only through your emotions; your environment is limited because of your immobility.

The BEHAVIORISTIC PERIOD – from your first to approximately your sixth year, during which your environment has been enlarged to include the rest of your home. You are now mobile and you are developing your imaginative faculty because you are developing your vocabulary. You are learning by observation and imitation of your parents, friends, and brothers and sisters.

The COGNITIVE PERIOD – through adolescence to adulthood. Now your environment has enlarged to include school and friends. It is during this period that you become conscious of peer pressure, the need to be like everyone else within your age group. How well you cope with this life experience depends largely on how well you were programmed during the affective period (made to feel secure by love experience such as hugging, petting) and the behavioristic period (given a sense of self-esteem by proper guidance, discipline and ego-stimulating assurances of identity).

Thus your response to any given situation within your environment may be dominated by any one of the above periods.

An example: A man demonstrates his objection to a piece of furniture his wife brought home by destroying it with a hatchet. This is obviously a child-like response (typical of this adult man who is emotionally immature) and the result of the dominance of his affective-period life experiences. Had he been dominated by his behavioristic-period programming, his reaction to the particular piece of furniture probably would have been the same. But his response would have followed whatever pattern of behavior he had been programmed for during his behavioristic period. Thus if his father was a meek, submissive person, this man would probably say nothing to his wife about intensely disliking the piece of furniture. Instead, he would sulk, avoid it, or at most would speak of it disparagingly. But he would not destroy it.

Had he been emotionally mature and dominated by his cognitive period, he could still object to the furniture in point – if he truly felt it out of keeping with the decor of the room. He would, however, have adopted a reasoned attitude and tried to reach a reasonable compromise by pointing out the obvious incompatability, the deficiency in its design perhaps, and suggest an alternative which would satisfy both his wife and himself.

This brief case history (the man had a hangup because he couldn't forgive his mother for abandoning him as a child when she died) is a dramatic summation of the NovaYoga postulate on the primacy of the love experience. It is not only most important to your early programming, but indeed, you never outgrow your need for love.

You Do Best What You Are Best Fitted to Do

First, NovaYoga training helps you overcome your hangups. But what are hangups exactly? A hangup is that causal factor within your subconscious which manifests itself as part of your personality pattern with a symptom such as excessive shyness, a stutter, obesity, or insomnia, even alcoholism or drug addiction.

The actual causal factor is usually traumatic life experiences which you probably forgot consciously after they occurred during your childhood. Feelings of rejection, of insecurity, of inferiority, of unworthiness, of inadequacy all stem from incidents that are often repeated and are so painful that you repress the memory of them. This repression doesn't rid your mind of the painful recollections which manifest themselves in such fundamental "feelings" mentioned. These feelings, in turn, manifest themselves in various ways, from shyness through such urges to retreat from reality as taking drugs or excessive drinking.

These personality symptoms are the result of early *conditioning;* the manifest symptom (stuttering, obesity, shyness) is a *conditioned reflex.* Lack of proper love experiences is the most frequent factor. However, there are many others, such as the traumatic experience of one young man who came to NovaYoga for help. He suffered through an embarrassing experience in the fourth grade when an unthinking teacher made fun of his mispronunciation of an unfamiliar word when reading aloud. The class laughed, and he was so embarrassed he ran from the classroom. So he came to me with a problem that had grown from this small beginning. He found it necessary, in his work, to address groups. The problem manifested itself in his inordinate fear of the public-speaking situation.

Whenever you see a person who is happy and successful in his life situation, you may safely assume that he/she is self-confident, self-assured, and has self-esteem. His self-image is certainly that of someone secure in his love experiences. Because he is the focus of someone who loves him (first his mother/she and later his wife) he can esteem himself. This doesn't infer narcissism, but rather a person with identity.

One of the most difficult problems of the emerging adult is the acceptance of a suitable and realistic goal in his life. Because of the catastrophic letdown in parental discipline, much of the Now generation was allowed to grow up to adulthood without intelligent, understanding guidelines. Many were permitted total freedom, but without guidance; without a model (strong, ideal father image) they found themselves unable to cope satisfactorily with their peers and with their environment.

For many, therefore, the outlet took the form of rebellion. But rebellion against what? The pat expression was "the corrupt establishment." And there was much that was corrupt. But the greatest corruption was the abandonment of parental authority and the guidance the growing psyche is in need of in order to develop wholesomely. The result is that many now feel inadequate, insecure, rejected, unable to find an ego-satisfying outlet for their innate talents, capabilities, and capacities.

Everyone is born with certain innate qualities. If he can determine what these qualities are, it is then possible to postulate *that one does best what one is best fitted to do.* Following is a true case that will illustrate this Nova-Yoga postulate.

Two boys living in Flushing, New York were graduating from junior high school. They were both 13, friends of long standing, about equally competent in scholastic attainment. One boy asked his father, "Dad, I'm going to high school next year – what do you think I should study for? What do you think I should be?"

His father answered, "Bruce, you have a great many capabilities. Tell me, what do *you* think you should be?"

Bruce grinned and said, "Well, I like sports best of all. I think I'd like to be a sports announcer."

His father said, "Fine. But before you make your decision, why don't we find out what you're best suited for."

Bruce was puzzled, "I don't know what you mean."

His father explained, "Everyone has certain talents, certain capabilities. If you're lucky enough to find your life's work in the area of your innate abilities, then it follows that you'll be happiest in doing that kind of work."

The boy was interested. "Well, I'm a good ballplayer and I like sports best. I should be the happiest as an announcer."

"I didn't say you wouldn't," his father replied, "but you'd be certainly more confident about your decision if you really knew you could do this kind of work best, wouldn't you?" Then he added, "A good way to find out so you'd be sure is to take an aptitude test. Wouldn't you like to take a few tests to find out what your natural aptitudes best suit you for?"

The boy agreed and his father arranged for his testing at a leading psychological testing laboratory in the city. The results of the tests were very revealing. They showed that, contrary to the boy's inclinations, he was *not* suited at all to be a sports announcer. His test results showed an aptitude for engineering.

Fortunately the boy was willing to follow the

guidelines his father offered him and accepted the advice of the testing psychologist. He went on to high school and college, achieving straight A's, and was awarded a fully paid fellowship at Princeton University where he earned his master's degree in high-polymer chemistry. He is now happily married, has two children, a beautiful suburban home, and is at the top of his profession.

But what about his boyhood friend? When Bruce was told about aptitude testing by his father he spoke to his friend and to his friend's father as well. His suggestion that both boys take the tests met with derision. The boy's father said *his* son had already decided he was going to be an engineer. He didn't need any fancy tests to make up *his* mind. The fact is that subsequently this boy was expelled from Brooklyn Polytechnic High School and when last heard of he was driving a newspaper delivery truck.

The point of this illustration is that it is rare indeed for any person to recognize his own innate capabilities. Aptitude testing, preferably at an early age, is one of the finest investments anyone can make in his future happiness. NovaYoga regards such testing as one of the best means of overcoming personality hangups. Remember: you do best what you are best fitted to do.

The Moment of Reality

This is the NovaYoga interpretation of the teaching of Epicurus who was schooled in the systems of Plato and Democritus. About 303 B.C. he established his famous Garden in Athens where he taught his followers.

The Epicurean philosophy was later (and erroneously) regarded as teaching a doctrine of refined voluptuousness. Actually, Epicurus was a conservative man who taught that pleasure (happiness) is the goal of all moral systems and that genuine happiness is derived from a life of prudence, honor, and justice. The founders of the United States, it appears, had something of this philosophy in mind when they wrote into the Declaration of Independence that you are entitled to life, liberty, and the pursuit of happiness.

If you can accept the postulate that happiness is the highest goal, you should also be able to accept the concept of *your* moment of reality, which is as follows:

Your life's experience consists of your perception of your past, your present, and your future. Surely you can accept as fact that your past, good or bad, is indeed past. There is nothing you can do about it other than try to correct whatever wrongs (unhappiness) you may have experienced. This cannot be done in your future because prudence tells us "never put off 'till tomorrow – because tomorrow never comes." It must therefore be corrected in the present.

Similarly, you must accept the premise that your future happiness depends on what you do *now* that makes you happy. If you do *now* that which will correct your past unhappiness (so that it makes you happy now), the chances are, such actions will insure your happiness in the future.

It becomes necessary for you to be happy *now,* to insure your happiness in the future. To honor this creed you must try to make every moment of your reality (the present) happy. If you will so live your life that every moment of your reality is happy, then all the facets of your life's experience will be happy.

If you think a little about this, you will soon begin to understand that your life does indeed consist of only this very moment of your physical (conscious) perception of yourself – in relation to your environment. Everything else lies within your mind. *Everything else is subject to interpretation by your imaginative faculty.* Your past is just a memory, while your future is conceived only within your imagination. You will begin to understand why

NovaYoga is the yoga of the imagination. You will begin to understand, too, the dynamism of this concept, that the vital force within you should be unrestrained, unfettered, uninhibited, that you should live every moment of your reality to the fullest of your innate talents, capabilities, and capacities.

Thus, whatever engages your perceptions (you perceive every moment of your reality with your five senses) you favor, you savor, and you labor for it with all the vital force at your command.

All about you are persons who are scurrying about their life's experience with their eyes downcast, their thoughts turned inward, living mechanically – instead of employing their five senses in perceiving their environment – enjoying, being happy, in every moment of their reality.

Since happiness is your life's goal, how can you attain it? A good start is to overcome whatever emotional problem presently inhibits you (get rid of your hangups). Since this problem probably had its inception in your early traumatic experiences, they are the evils that you will overcome – now – in your present moment of reality. (You are doing this now by applying yourself to NovaYoga.)

Next, you will live your present without allowing your future to pose a burden. This doesn't mean that you will enjoy every moment being as irresponsibile as a child. On the contrary. The NovaYoga view of Epicurean philosophy is that you seek (as ultimate happiness) that emotional maturity which is possible through positive ego-development. It is the emotionally mature person who is free of inhibiting hangups, free of repressing compulsions, free to fully enjoy each moment of his life's experience as a well-integrated personality, independent of peer pressure, self-confident, self-assured, and with self-esteem.

You will learn how best *you* can live this philosophy

as you pursue your study of the NovaYoga technique of self-realization.

Summary

You now have the rationale on which NovaYoga – yoga of imagination – is based:

> Your life's goal is happiness.
> You never outgrow your need for love.
> You do best what you are best fitted to do.
> Your moment of reality – you learn how to employ your imagination – to become the person you want to be.

Chapter 2

How You Developed Your Present Personality

YOU WERE BORN with certain innate talents, capabilities, and capacities. Everyone begins life with his genetic inheritance, which includes not only his unique physical characteristics, color of hair, eyes, etc., but his intelligence and natural aptitudes.

There is nothing you can do about any of these inherited characteristics except use them to attain that happiness (self-realization) which is your goal in life.

Your ability to make full use of your natural endowments, however, is qualified by the kind of the conditioning experiences you were exposed to during your formative years.

It would help, perhaps, if you will think of your brain as a computer into which information is programmed daily. There is already a certain amount of programmed information in your brain/computer when you are born. For example, deep within your subconscious lies the mechanism, already programmed, that controls the autonomic functioning of your viscera and the sympathetic nervous system. No one has to train you to breathe or to circulate your blood or to activate the peristaltic action of your alimentary canal. These functions are classified as involuntary; they are purely physical.

As you will soon begin to learn, though, your emotional reactions to your environment have a decided effect on these so-called involuntary actions. What are your emotions? These are affective states of consciousness: love and hate, joy and sorrow, and so on. They differ from cognitive or volitional states of consciousness and are characterized by certain physiological changes such as an increased heartbeat or crying.

Fear is a powerful emotion which triggers physiological reactions. It is related to your instinct for survival. The moment you are threatened, you experience an emotion called fear, which sets off a chain reaction that affects your glandular system, with the result that your bloodstream is charged with an excess of sugar. This sugar is reduced to glucose and burned directly in the muscles to provide the muscular energy – to fight or flee.

When you are born, there are indications that only two stimuli create a fear reaction – a loud noise and the sense of falling. This can be rationalized as instinctual fears stemming from racial heritage that goes back to the time when our primeval ancestors lived in trees. All other fears you learn, only too quickly.

Such learning is the basis of your "conditioning" or "programming" and is the individual characteristic the sum of which constitutes your personality. The manner in which such characteristics are developed is readily understood in the case of a young man who came to me for training to relieve tension. He suffered severely from allergies caused by cats.

During introspection the man was able to recall that his mother had always cautioned him against cats because she was afraid of them herself. When he was six years old he was frightened when a cat jumped at him unexpectedly, scratching him as he wildly tried to brush it away. (He had previously been "programmed" by his mother to fear cats, and now he had the experience of a trauma to create the causal factor for what later developed into a full-blown allergy when he was forced to live in an apartment adjoining one where two cats were kept as pets.)

Your Mind—Conscious and Subconscious

According to Freud, there are several aspects of the human mind. It will be helpful to list them here.*

The deepest, most primitive area – the source of

---

* It is interesting to compare the latest findings of modern cerebronauts with the theories of Freud. In 1973, the latest publication reporting the discoveries of brain scientists, entitled *Discovering Yourself in the Brain Age*, issued by the U.S. Department of Health, Education and Welfare, reveals that the human brain is not one but three! It is composed of the primitive, reptilian brain, referred to as the *old brain* which is the source of "instinctual" urges such as finding a mate, establishing a home, defending oneself and one's territory, to hunt for resources. This, it appears, would parallel Freud's "libido."

There is the neocortex referred to as the *new brain*. This is known to involve conscious sensations, bodily movement and thinking. This is the area of your perceptions, your five senses. Mental images and conceptions such as ideas, opinions, thoughts, or knowledge exist here in a complex arrangement of electrical/chemical activity. This could be assumed to parallel Freud's "super-ego."

The third brain is the *limbic brain* which serves as a mediator between the old and new brains. This is involved in emotional behavior and integrates information coming from inside or outside the body. And this could be assumed to parallel Freud's "ego."

Additionally, there is a small cluster of cells known as the hypothalmus, near the bottom of the brain, which are involved in states of anxiety, fear, anger, or more pleasant emotions such as happiness and serenity. Finally, there is an arousal system called the reticular formation located between the old brain and the spinal cord. This seems to be constantly involved in a kind of conversation with your new brain and other parts of your body for purposes of instant arousal, to alert your body when your new brain suddenly relays the message "fire!"

the primal urge, the libido, instinctive energy, the source of self-preservation, of self-satisfaction, the emotional core – was designated as the id. This is the area of the passions and the sex drive. As an infant you were dominated by this primitive drive. You wanted a great deal of tactile manifestation of love – petting, hugging, kissing – to give you the feeling of security.

If your mother was a demonstrative person, you received the love experiences you craved. Many adult hangups stem from this period when they either received too little or too much love experience. Feelings of insecurity, which develop into feelings of inferiority and inadequacy, become the basis of the adult *underachiever.* When subsequent traumatic experiences reinforce this early programmed material, a *negative self-image* may be created and an entire system of negative symptoms can develop.

Above this primitive level is that area of your mind which is in contact with your reality – your environment. This is the ego, which is the expression of your personality, the image you present to your world. All of your programming experiences, which you receive during your affective, behavioristic, and cognitive periods, affect or modify this image. If you are shy or self-conscious, with feelings perhaps of inadequacy and inferiority, you will present an image to the persons within your environment of a quiet, shy, introverted personality.

Your self-image will determine the ego-image you present to the world. As Solomon said, "As a man thinketh in his heart, so is he."

Above this level is still another, which is known as your super-ego. This is your moral guide and censor. It is the mechanism that comes into play to help modify the often unrestrained demands that bubble up from your primitive id. This area is not developed fully during your affective period, but it becomes more and more the factor that will guide your development as you have more and more life experiences.

During your affective period (your first year) it was your mother who totally dominated you. She was the only source of security. If she was a wise and loving person, she provided you with intelligent disciplinary guidelines, which not only made you feel perfectly safe and secure but gave you the basis for developing your identity. Although as an infant you had no frame of reference to enable you to communicate and to consciously understand the action within your environment, you did learn quickly how best to obtain satisfaction when you were hungry or uncomfortable. This was all accomplished with your emotional responses, although every day you programmed yourself more and more, learning how to coordinate your fingers and hand movements, learning to recognize familiar objects (your mother first of all), gradually training yourself, programming your marvelous computer.

Your programming, remember, began with the moment of your birth. Despite this fact a great many mothers or adults say and do things within the conscious grasp of the infant, remarking, "Oh, he's only a baby, he can't understand!" They should read *Rebel Without a Cause, The Hypnoanalysis of a Criminal Psychopath,* by Robert M. Linder. They will learn how a child, in his crib, was programmed by fear when he was awakened and witnessed his parents in intercourse. This became the causal factor which, reinforced by subsequent events in this boy's life experiences, led him to prison as a criminal psychopath.

Your affective period begins to change when you begin to change your environment. Usually, for the first year you are limited to wherever your mother places you. Being immobile, you spend most of your time programming yourself – playing with your fingers, moving your hands and legs, generally learning how to coordinate your bodily movements. These are the primary biofeedback procedures. You had to program your computer with an almost incredible number of actions and reactions, involving many different areas of your brain and affecting many different areas of your musculature.

Eventually, usually after about a year of this, you learned how to crawl and then walk, and with these achievements your environment began to expand into your behavioristic period. This period usually covers the time from your first year to your sixth. You begin the cognitive period with another meaningful change in your environment, when, after your sixth year, you expand socially to include school and outdoor experiences.

It is during your behavioristic period that you program yourself with the basic behavioristic pattern that is characteristic of your family environment. The old folk saying, "monkey sees, monkey does," applies here because it is how you learn and how you program yourself. Eventually, because you usually pattern yourself after your parent (boys after their fathers, girls after their mothers), you develop the subconscious self-image that will influence the development of your ego.

Finally you reach the cognitive period (although this is not actually your final stage for development, inasmuch as your programming never stops and continues with each environmental change). This period should lead you through adolescence to adulthood and on to maturity.

Becoming an adult does not necessarily mean that you will become mature. (Go back to the case of the man who destroyed his wife's furniture because he disliked it.) He was obviously an adult, but he was not a mature adult. He was a childish adult, always responding as a child would respond to every event occurring within his environment.

A Traumatic Experience

A traumatic experience is a "painful" experience, something you react to emotionally and find it causes you fear, anxiety, sometimes actual physical pain. It is because the experience does have a deeply emotional, painful impact that it remains deeply imbedded in your memory bank. An example can be cited from the *Autobiography of Benvenuto Cellini.* When Cellini was a small boy his father called to him one day. "Benvenuto, Benvenuto – come!" The boy ran to his father who was pointing to the fire that was flaming in the fireplace. His father cried, "Look, Benvenuto, look – what do you see?" The boy at first could see nothing but the flames, and then he exclaimed, "Yes, papa, I see – I see something – something that looks like a lizard." With that his father slapped him hard on his cheek. The boy cried, "Papa, why do you slap me?" His father replied, gravely, "So that you will never forget that you have seen the fabled salamander disporting in our fire!"

Cellini never forgot the incident, just as as you never forget any painful incident you experience during your affective, behavioristic, or cognitive periods. (Remember, all your life experiences are programmed into that computer of yours.) Experiences that are accompanied by some deep emotion or by actual pain are recorded more vividly; they can, and often do, become the causal factors that stimulate an adult personality hangup (which you are now trying to overcome).

The Conditioned Reflex

In 1904 Pavlov conducted his experiments on the salivating of dogs. By means of ingenious instrumentation, Pavlov was able to measure accurately the amount of salivation as well as the gastric juices of a number of test dogs. His experiments were based on each dog being exposed to food, which would instantly start the process of salivation with subsequent gastric implementation. Having established his basic charts, he proceeded to expose the dogs to food while ringing a bell. These charts matched the originals perfectly. Finally he only rang the bell and checked as before. He discovered that the amount of salivation and gastric juices was the same. The dogs had been conditioned (programmed), and their responses were called a *conditioned reflex.* For this work Pavlov was awarded the Nobel Prize. The importance of his findings to everyone today who is seeking to overcome some vexing personality problem or hangup cannot be overestimated.

A typical case in point (which can serve as an example of a conditioned reflex personality problem) is that of a young man of 28 who came to me for training in relaxation. Studying the manual, he learned the principle of introspection and revealed the basis for his present tensions. (His personality problem was a deep-seated feeling of inferiority.) He recalled that when he was very little he used to hang around his mother a great deal, and she, unthinking and perhaps pettishly, said to him over and over: "Why can't you be like Harry [his older brother]? Harry's wonderful! He's so popular. Everybody loves Harry. Why can't you go out and play like Harry?"

You can readily understand that if you were genetically constituted to prefer creative pursuits which imposed more solitude, and you were told day after day by the important authority-figure, your mother, that Harry, your brother, was wonderful, and that you were not, it wouldn't take very long for you to become totally programmed to a self-image of yourself as an inferior person.

Introspection

Introspection is the process of examining your mind, your emotions, your memory of experience – yourself. It begins when you begin a revery in which you see yourself at a particular time and place, and then, by a process Freud called free-association, related imagery presents itself.

To enable you to satisfy yourself as to the causal-factor experiences you had as a child, you will begin consciously to make such recall. If you find it difficult to dredge up such early material, don't worry. You will do better once you have trained yourself in meditative relaxation, a wonderful procedure for relaxation which you will learn later in your study of NovaYoga.

Introspection during meditative relaxation is called *age regression* and is accomplished only in the totally relaxed state of consciousness. However, following the methods of behavioristic psychology, it may not be necessary to recall *every* traumatic experience and identify it as the causative factor. All that is required is your understanding and acceptance of the principles involved. In this case, you accept as fact that the cause of *your* particular personality problem (underachieving, obesity, insomnia, whatever) began with your earliest programming. Now, whether or not you can remember the *actual* incidents, you must accept that they are indeed the cause of your present problem. As to who was responsible – your mother or father or anyone else – you probably have some feeling who it is. Assuming for the moment that it was your mother, you proceed with a process called rationalization.

Rationalization

Rationalism is the principle of accepting reason as the supreme authority in matters of belief. Philosophically, reason alone is the source of knowledge – independent of experience. Hence because it is well known, empirically, that a personality problem which manifests itself as a stutter or an inordinate shyness, feelings of inferiority, inadequacy, or simply underachieving stem from early conditioning (programming), which results in the creation of a negative self-image. By applying rationalism, we learn that it is evident that if the negative self-image is the cause, then a *reconditioned* self-image – a positive self-image of the person you want to be – will result in a new, reconditioned reflex.

Therefore, recognizing and accepting that you did create a negative self-image during your formative period, you now create a positive self-image of the person you truly want to be. By following the detailed instructions given in Chapter 12, you can recondition yourself, employing this new, positive self-image.

Assuming, however, that during introspection you *do* recall the traumatic incident or incidents which appear to be the causal factors for your present problem, test to learn if there is a reasonable parallel between that incident and your present problem.

For example, a young man who had an important job as a chemist had a peculiar symptom. He was unable to pick up a glass of water or a cup of coffee when with someone without spilling most of it because his hand would shake uncontrollably. An exact parallel was found during introspection when he recalled the time his mother brought home his newborn sister. He was three years old at the time and deeply resented this newcomer; he shook both fists at the baby to vent his anger.

Rationalization enabled him to accept the obvious

fact that his shaking hand merely represented repressed anger. He then followed the procedure given in Chapter 12, visualized himself giving vent to his anger as a child, and through rationalism, reasoned that *as a child* he had had to repress his anger, but that *now* it was no longer necessary to so repress anger. He bought a punching bag and installed it in his garage. Every evening after work he would take off his coat, go to the punching bag and there give complete vent to all the anger that had been building up during the day.

It is possible, of course, that your introspection will not enable you to recall an exact parallel incident. A young woman came to me to learn how to meditate to attain peace of mind from depression. She had deep feelings of inferiority. Her mother had rejected her soon after birth by placing her with a foster home. She had been cruelly informed of this when she was seven and placed in a school. Her reaction was to cry herself to sleep. She subsequently became excessively shy and self-conscious. She had developed a negative image of herself as being unloved and rejected.

There are many incidents possible. You will recognize one either because of its unhappy, painful effect on you emotionally or you will satisfy yourself that there is a deeply buried incident, the exact nature of which is too painful for you to dredge up, and apply your adult rationalism: that the circumstances *then* no longer apply *now*. That the image created then will now be altered to the positive image of the person you want to be.

The principle will apply to *any* personality problem. Once you have satisfied yourself, either with direct recall during introspection or by reason of the fact, empirically proven, that all hangups have the programmed causal factors buried in early life experience – and whether you succeed in recall or not the procedure is the same – create your new, positive self-image, and by

Pavlovian iteration and reiteration, wipe out the negative self-image and replace it with your new, positive self-image, as is explained in Chapter 12.

Summary

You are born with innate talents, capabilities, and capacities.

Your mind (the programming you receive) is developed during three periods – the affective period, the behavioristic period, and the cognitive period. With an understanding of these periods, you should eventually reach emotional maturity.

However, traumatic experiences (your love or lack of sufficiently satisfying love experiences) can cause a negative self-image which will manifest itself in a personality problem you wish to overcome.

Using introspection you can learn of these experiences or accept the fact of such experiences, and then through rationalization create your new, positive self-image. By a Pavlovian process of iteration and reiteration, this image wipes out the negative image, thus enabling you to act, to be the person you want to be.

Because of that unique characteristic of the human brain – the imaginative faculty – you possess an awesome power for good or evil. It can make you ill (as a result of conditioned hangups) or well (as a result of reconditioned positive self-imagery).

As a man thinketh in his heart, so is he.

Chapter 3

How to Improve Your Blood Circulation by Stretching

For optimum results it is suggested that you read the entire book, much as you would a novel, before you begin with the exercises, both physical and mental. You will enter upon the training in the NovaYoga technique of self-realization with the enthusiasm of a true believer, ensuring your success. Return to this chapter and establish your routine when you have completed your first reading.

LET'S FACE IT — no one likes exercises. But I'm betting you'll like these because you do them lying down! You don't move a muscle at first, yet you'll be more relaxed than you've been since you were a baby.

There are some 84 postures and exercises in classic hathayoga, most of which are virtually impossible of attainment except for those who began to practice them in early childhood. Of the 84, however, only 7 are important to you in applying NovaYoga. They were selected solely for their effectiveness in promoting visceral health and improving blood circulation. Remember, NovaYoga is the yoga of imagination, and we are interested in promoting the health of your body in order to promote the health of your brain, which requires a constant flow of good, rich blood with the proper balance of oxygen and glucose.

You are urged to practice the exercises given below. They are extremely simple and involve little physical strain. In fact, the object of each exercise, except for the first one, called muscular repose, is merely to stretch certain muscles. It is in the gentle stretching of these muscles that you will exercise your viscera and thereby promote blood circulation.

It is not important that you attempt to master each exercise immediately. Obviously, some will be a little more difficult than others, but unlike exercises that are designed to *strengthen* your muscles, these are intended to be performed slowly, easily, without strain. The moment you do feel strain, you should stop and return to the first posture – muscular repose.

It is recommended that these exercises be done the first thing every morning right after you have left the bathroom – and before you have your breakfast. (I can hear many of you groan already.) As with any school of yoga, if you hope to master the discipline and gain the benefits that NovaYoga can bring to you – starting with that blessed release of all your tensions and leading to that state of normal consciousness wherein you are truly tranquil – you must expect that you will have to make some effort, some sacrifice, and some change in your present mode of living.

After all, aren't you studying NovaYoga because your present life, your present mode of living, hasn't given you that peace of mind, that feeling of tranquility, that opportunity to achieve self-realization? Don't be alarmed. You will not be asked to become a renunciate, as many yoga schools require. The change you seek is first, to overcome some inhibiting personality characteristic, which will then allow you to become the person you want to be. Very well, that is precisely what NovaYoga offers: the opportunity for you to overcome your negative self-image and to condition you to a new and positive self-image, which will enable you to achieve personal self-realization.

So if the rewards offered are so great, surely the relatively small amount of sacrifice you are asked to make to attain that reward is a small price.

These exercises need not take more than 15 minutes every morning. Set your alarm for a half-hour earlier than your usual time. You'll have the fifteen minutes needed for the exercises plus a few minutes more for the simple breathing that follows.

Once you've begun this regimen, you will feel such an increased sense of physical and mental well-being that you will want to do as many students do, exercise first thing in the morning and then again in the evening.

When you begin the exercises do not try to perform all seven at once. Always start with muscular repose, then do the first three, then stop. And don't try to perfect each exercise the first time or even during the first week. Each day, perhaps, you can add another exercise so that, say, during the first week you will do the basic muscular repose plus three, then plus four, then plus five, until you can easily do all seven exercises comfortably in the time allotted. Soon – very soon – you will find that you are able to zip through all of them expertly, follow up with brief, deep breathing, and go off to breakfast with an improved appetite.

What is important is *routine*. Once you have set the time each day for these exercises, you should stick to it until it becomes a habit – a conditioned reflex. We are creatures of habit. We easily fall into routines. You will find it is as easy to form good habits as it is to overcome bad ones. Applying yourself to NovaYoga is going to help you overcome a lot of bad habits, by training you to new good habits.

You will quickly learn to start your day at the highest peak of your capacity. You will have the drive, the motivation, to go about your day's work feeling exhilarated, functioning at the highest level of your innate capabilities, giving you an enormous boost in self-confidence, self-assurance, and self-esteem.

A final word before you begin. There is virtually no one totally free of tension who will be studying NovaYoga. Your own tension may not be apparent consciously, yet the moment you become conscious of your subliminal thoughts, you realize that you are indeed tense subconsciously. These exercises can be considered *somatopsychic*; that is, they will eventually relax your body so completely that it will result in mental relaxation.

In classic hathayoga you are told to make your mind a blank. Well, that is virtually impossible – until you are trained to mantra meditation. It is the stress-producing thoughts that presently dominate your subconscious and which cause your tension. You are urged, therefore, to apply yourself simultaneously to both the physical exercises and the breathing exercises, because in practicing breathing, you will also begin the practice of concentration.

While it is virtually impossible to make your mind a blank, it is possible to train your imaginative faculty to concentrate on a symbol of some sort – to eliminate conflicting imagery. In the next chapter, on training in deep breath control, you will learn how to concentrate on the Yin/Yang black-and-white symbol. The Yin and Yang is employed because it is peculiarly appropriate. In ancient Chinese philosophy the Yin and Yang were the two principles of negative (dark) and positive (white); their interacting influence affected one's destiny.

In the first exercise of muscular repose you will be directing your imaginative faculty to the various muscles of your body, to control their total relaxation in order to reach a state of near collapse. In the subsequent exercises no such imaginative control is suggested. If, however, when you begin your practice of these exercises, you find that you are tense because of stress-producing imagery within your subconscious (which makes you tense), you will concentrate on the Yin/Yang and eliminate the conflicting imagery.

Complete relaxation can be attained by following the proper exercise procedure. To attain this relaxation you will visualize the Yin/Yang during each exercise while silently verbalizing "I am at peace – fully relaxed."

Muscular repose

All exercises are best performed while lying on a hard floor with perhaps a carpet or mat as the floor covering. A soft bed will not provide the same results. Breathe naturally and try to *feel* your muscles slowly giving in to the hardness of the floor.

First, you will feel your spine loosening and sagging to the floor. Slowly all of your muscles will feel as though you are in a state of total collapse.

This exercise is completely passive; that is, you need do nothing more than exercise your imagination. Begin by first closing your eyes and then consciously visualizing each muscle relaxing, starting with your feet. Tense your toes – as though trying to pick up a wash cloth from the floor – then let them relax. As they relax, *feel* the relaxation, *visualize* the relaxation. Your feet, up to each ankle, will feel loose, limp, collapsed.

Continue on up to your calves, to your knees. Tense the muscles first, then let them relax. Again, feel and

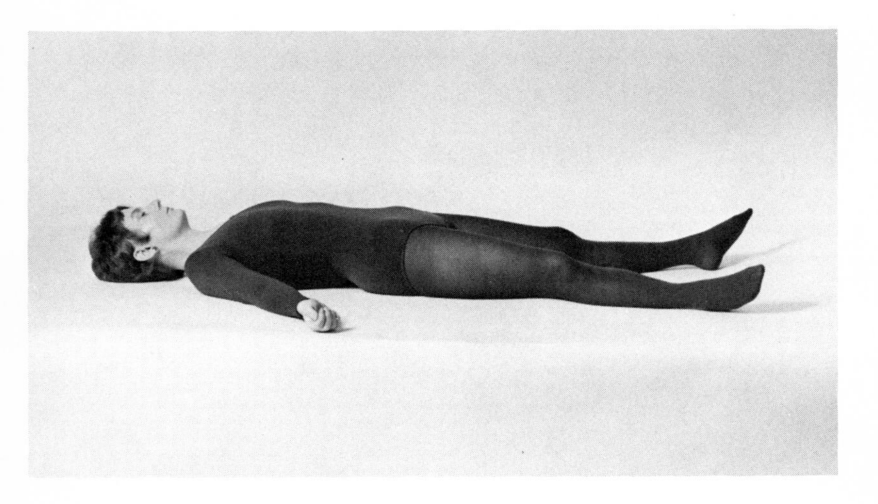

visualize the relaxation. Now your feet and your calves will be in a state of utter collapse.

Continue in exactly the same manner to your thighs; then your back, shoulders, arms, hands, and fingers; then your neck, head, face, jaw, and throat; finally to your chest and to all the organs within your body. *Feel* yourself in a state of complete collapse. It will be easier if you are on a hard floor, because the hardness, in a few minutes, will act as a powerful magnet for all your muscles, drawing them down into a state of collapse.

When you have reached this physical state of relaxation, remain passive for a moment longer. Use your imagination as follows: if you are overweight, *visualize* yourself as the person you want to be – slim, wearing that dress you like or those slim jeans and that form-fitting leather jacket. Let your mind fantasize (you will learn creative revery in a later chapter).

Remember, NovaYoga is the yoga of the imagination. Every exercise is an exercise in directing, controlling, your imaginative faculty. Your fantasy, when you have achieved total physical and mental relaxation in muscular repose, is to follow your motivation, that is, the image of the person you want to be. If you stutter, visualize yourself making a speech. More important, try to actually *feel* the emotion of complete triumph, being congratulated, bowing to the enthusiastic applause, being totally successful. By the same token – whatever your motivation may be – when you have attained total physical relaxation in muscular repose, follow it up immediately with *positive imagery* of yourself being happy, being self-confident, being self-assured, and having enormous self-esteem.

Just a word about *visualization.* One young woman began to cry when she was told to visualize herself in her mind's eye. When asked what the trouble was, she said, "I don't *see* anything in my mind's eye." So a word of advice: not everyone will be able to actually see the mental imagery, as though looking at a movie. But you *will* be able to visualize quite satisfactorily before you finish this book – providing, of course, that you practice. However, the fact is that everyone possesses an imaginative faculty. You may not have consciously used it as you are being trained to use it now; therefore your imagery may not be as vivid photographically. But, rest assured, the imagery is there. Just go ahead – think the instructions – talk to yourself mentally. The images will do their stuff.

Raised leg exercise

This is the first exercise that follows, naturally, muscular repose. You are lying flat on your back, inhaling naturally. Raise your right leg slowly, without bending the knee. At first you will not be able to raise it fully as in the illustration; do the best you can without straining. When your effort begins to strain the leg muscles, stop and bring your leg down slowly.

Then slowly start to raise the other leg without bending it at the knee. Again bring it up only as high as you can without straining.

Next, raise both legs together, again without bending them at the knees. Here you will probably feel your arms pressing down on the floor. Raise your legs as high as you can without strain and bring them back again – slowly.

As with any new exercise, if you are doing it for the first time, you will probably feel slightly fatigued, despite

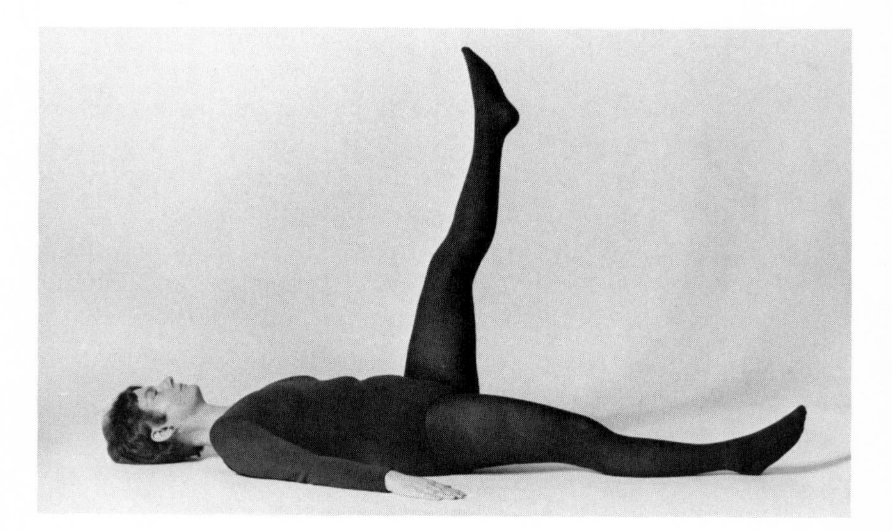

the fact that you've done very little so far. Remember that you are not training yourself as though in a gymnasium. What you have done so far has been excellent. Without your thinking about it, the muscles of your diaphragm have been stretched and your viscera has been exercised. If your abdominal muscles feel a little sore, it simply means that you've allowed yourself to become excessively soft and flabby. The soreness will quickly disappear. At first raise your legs only a very few times. Later, in a week or so, you'll be amazed how easy this exercise becomes.

The raised leg exercise, as are those that follow, is excellent for the abdominal muscles. Performed daily (or better, twice daily), these exercises will help considerably in breaking down excess fat.

If your normal daily routine is sedentary and you use your abdominal muscles very little, you will be delighted when you find, quite soon, that you have a flat stomach – that slim, trim look.

As with all exercises, caution must be taken. If you have any physical problem, if you have a heart condition, or for any reason whatever that makes you cautious about physical exertion, show your doctor these instructions and follow his advice.

Unless you are physically perfect and have been exercising regularly, it is suggested that you go at these exercises gradually. As mentioned above, all you are expected to accomplish at first is muscular repose, followed by the first three exercises, moderately performed. After that, as you begin to feel more competent, add another exercise, then another and another, until you are able to perform all seven exercises without feeling winded, and instead, feeling exhilarated.

The plough exercise

Since you are still lying on your back, the next logical exercise is the plough. Starting always with muscular repose, you should be in position, with your arms stretched out along your body.

In the plough, you begin by raising both legs together as you did in the raised leg exercise. The plough is a little more advanced. Here you will raise both legs to approximately 45 degrees and hold them in that position as long as you can, starting with five seconds. Then raise them to a full 90 degrees and hold them there for another five seconds. Finally, slowly allow both legs to continue beyond the 90-degree vertical position until, if possible, they are as far as shown in the illustration.

Your knees must remain stiff at all times and your hands (palms down) pressed flat on the floor for support. Because this is a more advanced exercise, you should master it slowly. Don't attempt to go the whole way the first time. When you feel strain, stop, go back to muscular repose, and rest a moment.

At first, you may not be able to hold the 45-degree

position at all. Try to go on, then, to the 90-degree position if you can. Let me emphasize at this point: you are not trying for an award. You are simply trying to master a few simple Hathayoga exercises. Go at them slowly, go a little further each day, and in a week or two you'll be going through them with ease.

The final position in this exercise is shown in the illustration. Don't be discouraged if you cannot reach this final position. The benefits are obtained, remember, by stretching. If you are young and supple, however, limber enough to be able to train yourself to this, then go ahead. Let your legs proceed beyond the 90-degree position until your toes touch the floor above your head. Count to 10 and then slowly raise your legs – back first to 90 degrees, hold for five seconds, then proceed down to the 45-degree position, hold there for another five seconds, then slowly lower your legs to the floor. You will be in the muscular repose position. Visualize the Yin/Yang, verbalize silently: "I am at peace, fully relaxed."

Your breathing should be regular throughout. Because this is a much more difficult exercise to perform, you will tend to bend your legs at the knees. Guard against this. The benefit you will enjoy from this exercise results from stiff legs (no bending) and hands glued to the floor.

Go at this exercise slowly, perhaps taking only the 45-degree position the first day. Next day, take both the 45-degree and the 90-degree. Stick with this for a few days, seeing each time how *slowly* you can bring your legs down. When this is perfected, try for the overhead position. If you never succeed in reaching the floor with your toes, don't consider it a failure. Don't overdo. Be a reasonable judge of your capability – then try to master this exercise slowly.

Eventually, if you persist, it will be one long s-t-r-e-t-c-h which you will enjoy very much.

The cobra exercise

As a change from exercising on your back, turn over on your stomach after completing the last exercise and lie face down with your forehead touching the carpet. Your arms should be bent, with your palms about level with your shoulders, which should be resting flat on the floor.

Stretch your legs, straight and stiff, the soles of your feet facing upward. As you begin, raise your head first, stretch your neck as much as you can so that your face is clear of the floor. Your chin will be pointing outward and you should feel the stretch in your neck muscles.

Then slowly, using the muscles of your arms, press down on your palms to raise your chest off the carpet. Try to use your back muscles to help in the raising, as much as the arm muscles; you should feel the pressure all the way down your spine.

This is not a push-up exercise. Your lower body, from the navel to the toes, will be resting on the floor. Arch your back and your head as much as you can until

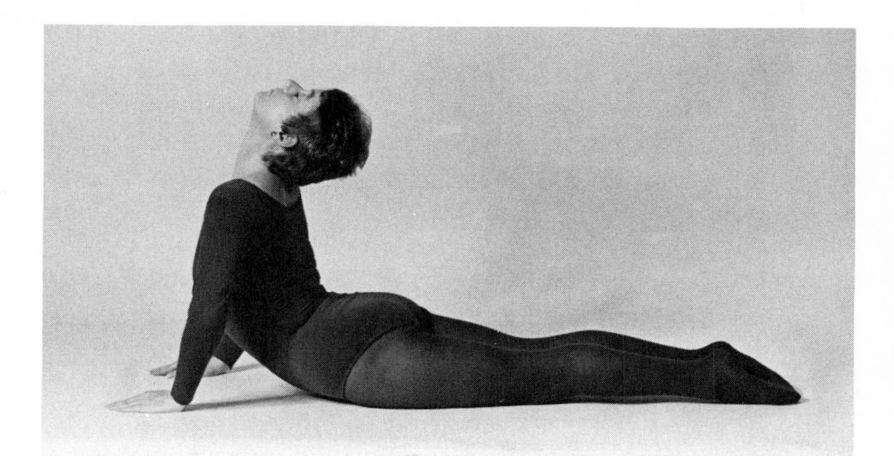

you begin to feel the strain of stretching. You should retain this position as long as you can without undue strain. In the position you will resemble a cobra posed to strike. With practice you will be able to increase the length of time you can retain the position from a few seconds to a minute or more.

Now slowly lower your torso to the floor. Lie face down for a moment and rest. Then repeat, while trying to raise your torso entirely with the muscles of your back. This will be difficult, of course, so you should push down on your palms to raise your torso, stretching your back muscles as you did earlier.

At first you will not be able to conceive of the possibility of doing this exercise without the help of your arm muscles. (Those who are adept, though, will be able to raise themselves entirely without pressing down on their palms.) But I caution you again – do not try to become an adept if you feel you haven't the capacity. Only if you are young and supple and have exercised regularly should you rely entirely on your back muscles.

Although you perform this exercise with the full use of your arm muscles, you should feel your back muscles contributing. The way to do this is to first raise your torso, using only the back muscles. Then, the moment you feel strain, press down on the palms and use your arm muscles to raise yourself fully.

As you can see, the exercises become increasingly more difficult. The object of the cobra exercise is to make your spine supple and flexible beyond anything you have ever known. This exercise and the jackknife exercise which follows are designed to flex your spine, to stimulate your spinal cord and thus help your central nervous system.

Proceed with these exercises slowly and cautiously. Never try to master any exercise immediately. Do a little more each day. Take your time. The reason the classic yoga school insists that you cannot learn without the help of a guru is because he will limit the amount and extent of your daily exercises, allowing you to practice slowly until your body has become sufficiently supple.

Each exercise is actually a pose. That is, each one should be performed as though in slow motion – steadily, smoothly, continuously, until you reach the ultimate. Pause, count to ten, then with equal deliberation return in slow motion – steadily, smoothly, continuously until your body is once more at rest.

The jackknife exercise

If you have ever seen a professional diver perform the famous jackknife dive, you have seen him assume this position in mid-air. It is difficult, obviously, unless your spine is very supple.

Begin the exercise with muscular repose. Bring your legs together, and then slowly raise your entire torso without raising your legs or bending your knees. This may sound impossible, considering your present physical condition. But you will be able to do it if you persist. Therefore, at first extend your arms in front of you as though you were reaching for a rod with which to pull yourself upright. This effort will help you raise your torso from the floor.

Exhale when you reach the sitting position. Then, with your arms extended forward, try to reach your ankles, gripping them as illustrated. You may never be able to reach this final position. Again, as in the previous exercises, much depends on your age and the suppleness of your body. If you realize that you cannot reach the ulti-

mate position, don't fret. Do the best you can. You will be surprised how far you will be able to stretch after you've done this exercise for a few weeks.

Bend forward as far as you can without jerking into position. Do it slowly and be satisfied with however much of a bend you can achieve. Go as far as you can until you feel a strain, then stop. Do not overextend yourself.

Try to hold whatever position you do achieve for five, maybe ten seconds, then slowly return to a sitting position. Then, just as slowly, lie back until you are stretched on the floor in muscular repose. Close your eyes, visualize the Yin/Yang, and verbalize silently: "I am at peace, fully relaxed."

The maximum benefit from this, as with all other exercises, is in acquiring a smooth, slow motion, pulling yourself forward a bit more each time you practice.

The cobra and jackknife exercises limber up the entire spine. When you understand that the nervous energy that starts within your brain is sent to all parts of your body via the bundle of nerves called your spinal cord and that between each of the 24 vertebrae in the cervical, dorsal, and lumbar regions, nerves branch out to reach all parts of your body, then perhaps you will appreciate why it is necessary to maintain suppleness in your spine. These bending and stretching exercises flex the cartilage that separates the individual vertebra and thereby stimulates the nerves that pass through to all parts of your body.

These exercises will aid considerably in strengthening and rejuvenating your body. Remember, I mentioned that the exercises chosen were those designed to strengthen your viscera, as well as the entire endocrine glandular system.

All excess fat will be gradually removed as you find yourself more and more flexible. These exercises, incidently, are equally beneficial to women as to men.

The bow exercise

This exercise may be considered an extension of the cobra position and can be performed in conjunction with the cobra exercise. When you have completed the cobra, you will be flat on your stomach with your arms bent so that your palms are about level with your shoulders.

Now stretch your arms so they are parallel with your sides. Now begin to bend your legs, forcing them back as far as you can, far enough to permit you to grasp your ankles. This isn't as easy as it sounds. You may have to cheat a little at first by reaching for only one ankle, twisting just a little so you can reach it. Then, holding onto your ankle, see if you can stretch a little on the opposite side so as to grasp the other ankle.

As with all of these exercises, you will find yourself able to accomplish what seems impossible at first – if you persist.

When you have hold of both ankles, pull your feet until you feel a strain. This movement will lift the knees

as well as the thighs off the floor; raise your head at the same time, as you did in the cobra. The object is to lie flat on your abdomen.

At first you will tend to spread your knees. Obviously, unless you are already trained, you will not be able to achieve the elevation shown in the illustration. But again, don't try for perfection immediately. The benefits come with routine. Do a little every day at the same time every day.

It is far better that you perfect the first movement before you try the second. Once you have mastered both movements, raising your chest as well as your thighs, you can learn to bring your knees together and thereby deepen your stretch.

These are all stretching exercises, that is, except for the muscular repose and the following shoulder stand. Muscular repose, as was explained, is most important, in that it serves to exercise your imaginative faculty and enable you to relax every nerve and muscle in your body. The shoulder stand that follows is purely to reverse gravity and to allow as much blood as possible to flow to your brain.

The cobra and now the bow are important basic exercises for the backward stretching of your spinal cord. These exercises, combined with the jackknife, give you the equivalent of a thorough chiropractic adjustment to your entire spine. However, exercise caution. Do not jerk yourself into position. Do not strain yourself. Do not, in short, do more than your body can reasonably attain, particularly if you are overweight. A little each day will do wonders!

The shoulder stand

The final exercise you are expected to practice in Nova-Yoga is the shoulder stand. While it is beneficial to your entire body, it is particularly beneficial to your brain, nourishing it with good, rich blood.

It is easier than it appears. You simply lie down in muscular repose, arms parallel to your body, palms down. Next, pressing down with your palms, raise both legs, bending the knees at the same time and raising yourself until your back is off the floor. While you are raising yourself, press down with your elbows and bring your hands to assist the small of your back to raise to the position shown.

You will be on your shoulders with your knees bent. The next movement obviously is to straighten out your knees, elevating your legs into the upright position as shown in the illustration.

When you begin you may be a little awkward trying to combine the several movements as explained. However, each of these movements is complementary to the others and you will find them entirely natural. After you have attempted this exercise only once or twice you will find that you can do it in one smooth, continuous, fluid movement.

In your final position you should have all your weight on your shoulders – back straight, neck bent as shown, arms bent, elbows pressing the floor, and hands supporting your back.

Give yourself an extra stretch by pointing the toes upward and trying to touch an imaginary point in mid-air. Hold this position as long as you can, at first, for only five to ten seconds. Eventually you will be able to maintain the posture for several minutes.

To reverse the procedure, first bend the knees, allowing your back to slip in your hands, then slowly descend to the floor. Your movement upward should be matched with equally slow, smooth movement downward. Allow your legs to straighten out as they reach the floor. Straighten out your arms, and you are in muscular repose.

Close your eyes, visualize the Yin/Yang, verbalize silently, "I am at peace, fully relaxed."

These are the seven simple exercises of NovaYoga. They are enormously beneficial, especially when combined with the breathing exercise that follows. You are urged to set aside two periods every day – in the morning after you have finished in the bathroom (having evacuated your bowels, go through as many as you can in 15 minutes) and later in the day, perhaps just after you arrive home from work, another 15 minutes.

At both times, it is important that you *follow the stretching exercises with the breathing exercises.* Open the window, stand in front of it, and follow the instructions in the next chapter.

Despite the simplicity of the stretching and breathing exercises, you will find, providing you are conscientious in your practicing, that in a very short time you will be experiencing a sense of physical and mental well-being you have never experienced before.

Chapter 4

How to Increase Your Mental Acuity by Breathing

OXYGEN IS A vital element without which you cannot exist. If you are denied this element for more than a few minutes, your brain, and therefore your body, will cease to function. Your bloodstream absorbs oxygen from the air you breathe, and this vitalizes all your tissues and organs.

It is so important to the maintenance of the health of your brain that if the carotid arteries on either side of your neck were to be compressed for only a matter of seconds you would black out. If the pressure were sustained, blocking passage of oxygen-carrying blood for some minutes longer, you could suffer brain damage and possibly death.

Under normal conditions, with every breath you take your body absorbs approximately 20 cubic inches of air. If the air you are breathing is deficient in oxygen the alertness of your brain (and your imaginative faculty) is impaired. A badly ventilated room can cause you to feel sluggish. You cannot study or think at your highest level when you are breathing air that is *stale*, deficient in oxygen.

There is, therefore, a sound basis for the yoga belief

that one's imaginative faculty (and hence, one's intellect) is affected by the supply of oxygen his body absorbs. Any malfunctioning of the breathing process – such as a stuffed or obstructed nasal passage due perhaps to an adenoidal condition, even a bad posture which fosters shallow breathing habits – can bring a lowering of the complete and effective functioning of your brain.

Proper breathing, therefore, is one of the prime requisites of NovaYoga. The physical exercises you studied (and are practicing), which were outlined in the previous chapter, stimulated your internal organs and increased your blood circulation.

Now, as you learn how to practice deep breathing, you will be adding vitalizing oxygen to your bloodstream and improving the health of your body, especially your brain. I mentioned earlier that on the average you inhale about 20 cubic inches of air with each breath. The exercise you will learn will enable you to increase this intake as much as five times!

You inhale oxygen and exhale carbon dioxide about 20,000 times a day. Under normal conditions this volume of oxygen provides your body and brain with the supply you need to maintain yourself within a normal social and physical environment.

However, if your breathing habits are bad, if you cannot inhale satisfactorily because of nasal obstructions, or if the air you are breathing is polluted (as it becomes frequently in our smog-ridden cities), your mind and body will not function at their highest levels. Consider what this can mean to your sense or feeling of well-being. Consider, too, what a lifelong habit of such bad breathing can do to impoverish your brain and hence help to cause hangups. You simply cannot function efficiently when your body and brain are functioning below par. Your biochemistry is altered, with the result that you may always feel inferior to those about you. Ours is a competitive society. If you consistently find yourself unable to compete, unable to respond satisfactorily to the demands of your environment, then it is easy to understand why, over a long period of time, you develop some negative self-image, which becomes the basis of your personality problem – your hangup!

Yoga has long recognized the tremendous importance of proper breathing. *Prana* is considered the primary vital force. *Pranayama* is the yogic science of breath control. There are five principal pranas and five *upa pranas,* or minor vital forces. As you can see, the classic yoga procedure is quite complicated and the training arduous.

NovaYoga has adapted the classic forms in breath control just as it has adapted the classic exercises of Hatha. While it is true that many years of training can give the individual yogi amazing control over his breathing, so that he is able to slow down his rate of respiration to a degree comparable to that of the hibernating animal – we are not interested in this much control. All we are concerned with is to increase the volume of oxygen in the bloodstream so as to provide your brain with that vital force that is used in developing and controlling the imaginative faculty. If you can learn a simple exercise that will increase your intake from a normal 20 cubic inches to a whopping 100 cubic inches, then, indeed, you will have sparked your brain capacity.

Proper breathing begins with inhalation through the nostrils, with your mouth closed. The mucous membranes act as a filter to remove most dust and germs. The air you inhale is therefore filtered and warmed before it enters your lungs and reaches the millions of cells that capture the air like microscopic sacs. The capillaries, or blood cells, absorb the fresh oxygen through the cell walls, exchanging the carbon dioxide which is then exhaled.

That marvelous pump, your heart, moves as much as 800 quarts of this freshly oxygenated blood through your lungs and all parts of your body – and your brain – every hour. As your body ages, your organs become somewhat less elastic or supple – hastened by years of improper breathing. But proper breathing helps your body remain healthfully young, slim, and vigorous. The yogi believes that those vague aches and pains which we have come to equate with advancing age result from all those years of improper breathing. Stiff joints, muscular pains, backaches, and the pain associated with rheumatism and neuritis are all thought to stem from years of improper breathing.

The Hatha exercises given in Chapter 3 are now to be combined with these exercises adapted from layayoga. Although all yogic pranayama exercises are essentially the same as those given here, in NovaYoga they are considerably simplified, the objective being to increase your oxygen intake.

NovaYoga Breathing Exercises

The object of the breathing exercises is to make you conscious of *the complete breath* and to urge you to practice it not only during your morning and evening Hatha exercise periods, but during the day, whenever you have a free moment.

Most of us, especially those engaged in sedentary work, are shallow breathers, breathing only with the upper top portion of our lungs. You can check yourself right now by doing this:

> Inhale deeply. Observe yourself. Did you expand your chest and contract your diaphragm? Probably you did. And this is precisely what you should not be doing.

Now you will learn what you *should* be doing. It is

called "diaphragmatic breathing," "thoracic breathing," and "the complete breath."

DIAPHRAGMATIC BREATHING

1] Stand in front of an open window. With your mouth closed, inhale deeply through your nostrils. Keep your chest rigid and concentrate your thoughts on your diaphragm. Let it expand as you count slowly (in your mind) to eight.
2] Hold your breath when you reach eight in your mental count, then count slowly to four.
3] As you let go your breath on the mental count of four, compress your diaphragm violently. Draw in your stomach muscles forcibly as you open your mouth to exhale with an audible "hu-u-u-h!"

The first time you practice diaphragmatic breathing you may find yourself coughing, especially if you are a smoker. Don't be alarmed. You are simply unused to deep breathing. Repeat the exercise six times. You may find, as most new breathers do, that the sixth breath causes a slight dizziness. This only confirms that you are unaccustomed to the absorption of this volume of oxygen. The oxygen that is absorbed quickly goes to your brain.

There is no need to actually continue beyond six inhalations the first time you practice this exercise. Counting mentally to yourself speedily establishes the rhythm. You will quickly accustom yourself to this rhythm – just don't strain!

The merit of all NovaYoga exercises is attained only with conscientious repetition. Do them over and over, twice each day as suggested. Accustom yourself to the routine and you will speedily master all the exercises, both Hatha and layayoga. You will find that in an amazingly short time you will be able to perform all the exercises and the breathing with great ease – and pleasure.

Your breathing habit is probably the oldest to which you have conditioned yourself. It is completely autonomic, controlled by your subconscious. It is rhythmical but probably in short and shallow breaths. But now you know of a simple deep-breathing exercise which assures you of ingesting upwards of 500 percent more oxygen. Give yourself an oxygen break at least twice each day when you've completed your Hatha exercises. Do more: whenever you have the chance – a moment before going out to lunch, a moment before dinner, whenever you think of it and have the opportunity to inhale fresh air – do so. Get into the habit of an oxygen break.

THORACIC BREATHING

1] Stand relaxed before an open window. Inhale slowly and deeply, concentrating on your rib cage. As you inhale, expand your chest, let it puff out, feel your shoulders and your entire chest expanding. Meanwhile, your diaphragm is rigid, stomach flat.

2] Begin the mental count to eight as your chest is expanding and your shoulders are spread. Hold your breath when you reach eight and while you count to four.

3] As you release your breath on the count of four, let your chest collapse and your shoulders shrink as you exhale with a violent "h-u-u-h!"

The purpose of the forced exhalation in both diaphragmmatic and thoracic breathing is to free your lungs of any trapped carbon dioxide and to prepare you for the following breathing, which can be deeper still.

This is not very different, you say, from the way you breathe normally? That's probably true. Most persons breathe with only the upper half of their thoracic lung area. The difference is the depth and the volume of air you are now able to ingest.

While it is quite true that the yogi adept at any classic form of yoga would snicker at this form of breathing (he having been trained to all 10 major and minor forms), remember that we are not concerned with becoming a yoga adept. We are concerned with sparking your brain with an oxygen cocktail during meditative relaxation, which you will learn in a later chapter.

THE COMPLETE BREATH

1] Again, before an open window (it helps to open two windows on opposite sides, if possible, to cause a draft), inhale slowly and deeply through your nostrils while counting to eight. You should concentrate first on your diaphragm and watch it expand, feel it expand.

2] Your diaphragm should be fully extended by the time you count to four. Then shift your concentration to your rib cage and see it, feel it, expand. Your shoulders should begin to spread.

3] When you have reached your silent count of eight, your entire diaphragm and thoracic area should be fully expanded with a total ingestion of air. Hold for a count of four – and then let go! As you let go, your exhalation compresses the muscles of your diaphragm and simultaneously compresses your rib cage and allows your shoulders to slump. Exhale with an audible "hu-u-u-h!"

4] Repeat this six times until you feel nicely exhilarated. After six complete breaths you may feel somewhat euphoric. As with all NovaYoga exercises, don't overdo it until you have practiced sufficiently to become adjusted and can perform all the exercises expertly and without strain.

Conscientious Practice

Because other aspects of NovaYoga are more glamorous – alpha rhythm, theta rhythm, biofeedback, mantra meditation, altered states of consciousness, astral projection, the center of tranquility – these Hatha and layayoga exercises tend to be sloughed over. I urge you not to skip any of them. You will get your reward when you arrive at the glamor stages, because you will be properly conditioned.

Habits are formed quite easily, as you know. It didn't take you long to acquire the smoking habit. It doesn't take any time at all to get into the habit of eating a sweet bun with a cup of coffee for breakfast. And in no time at all, you're looking forward to that cocktail every evening before dinner.

Habits. One can make you a caffeine addict. Another can make you fat. Still another can lead you to alcoholism.

It's just as easy to acquire good habits. First tell yourself that you are starting a brand new way of life, a way that promises to lead you to attainment of self-realization and happiness. Determine, therefore, that you will practice the Hatha exercises before breakfast every morning, followed by the deep-breathing exercise, and that you will repeat the exercises every evening before dinner.

I will offer you an unqualified guarantee. In a matter of a few short weeks you will experience a sense of physical and mental well-being such as you have never experienced before! And you will derive total benefit from the whole of NovaYoga training in all aspects, to become the person you want to be.

Chapter 5

How to Concentrate and Stop Grasshopper Dreaming

THUS FAR YOU have had, in actual training, Hatha and layayoga exercises to stimulate your blood circulation and oxygenate your blood. Both exercises are calculated to improve the health of your brain, the organ of imagination.

As man evolved, his brain developed that mechanism we can recognize in action as imagination and calculation, and with these he developed the ability to reason abstractly. The chimpanzee, which is the closest to man on the evolutionary scale, is unable to retain imagery so as to be able to reflect. Man alone is able to reflect on possible alternates, interpret responses to stimuli, and conceive imagery to overcome environmental limitations. *Cogito ergo sum* is not only philosophically but psychologically true.

Because of this marvelous faculty the human brain has been compared to a computer. The comparison is apt. When you consider that your brain contains between 10 and 12 billion neurons (brain cells), with each neuron emitting an electrical discharge (functioning as a switch in a man-made computer), you can understand why it would be beyond man's present technology to conceive of a computer with this number of switches.

But consider what happens when a computer goes awry. When the switches are uncontrolled, as for example, when a person receives a check for $1,000,000 when he was entitled only to a check for $100. This, in effect, is what happens in your brain when your imaginative faculty is similarly uncontrolled.

From the moment of your birth, your brain records images, impressions, experiences, and emotional responses to everything you perceive with your five senses. These recordings are in the form of images and constitute your "memory bank." This is how traumatic experiences become the basis for later personality hangups. When the incident is extremely painful or when it is the result of a repeated series of incidents, a larger number of neurons are impressed with these images. The larger the number of neurons impressed with the imagery of any given experience, the more readily available are such impressions for recall.

As Freud discovered, however, such impressions often are so painful to the psyche that they are repressed, consciously "forgotten." Nevertheless, they remain impressions and become instantly available at the subliminal level.

Just as with the man-made computer going awry because of some switching or electronic malfunction, so too is it possible for your imaginative faculty to flood your mind with apparently unrelated imagery *at the very moment when you are trying to concentrate.* The switches in the computer are uncontrolled, so the images that lie within your memory bank become uncontrolled and cause a comparable "malfunction," thus preventing you from concentrating your thoughts on one image.

Students often complain that they are unable to study, that they are unable to concentrate. When the computer analogy is explained to them they understand, but the question is the same – "How can we learn how to concentrate?"

Let us examine the problem. First, what is "concentration"? Concentration is the focusing of the imaginative faculty on *one* thought problem – allowing *only* such imagery to intrude that is *related* to the primary thought problem. Freud called such related imagery *free association*. By training his subjects to immediately describe the image or cite the first word that appeared in their minds in response to a particular question, he was able to train them in free association. His claim was that if the subject did not censor his response by "thinking" about it, but instantly gave his response, this would constitute a genuine "related" word or image.

Following this procedure as a principle of training the mind, NovaYoga training in concentration has proved most effective. There are two parts to the training which take into consideration the two aspects of the phenomenon. One is to learn how to control the flood of imagery that intrudes when you try to concentrate. The second is to learn how to direct the mind to the control of "free association" imagery that relates to the thought problem.

The first part of this training will be discussed in this chapter. The second part will be considered in Chapter 6.

If you were to have the electrodes of an electroencephalograph attached to your scalp, a record of your brain waves would be visible. There are four brain-wave patterns that have been identified as having distinct characteristics (mentioned in Chapter 1). The brain-wave patterns are recorded in the waking as well as the sleep stages, to prove that your brain is constantly functioning, that is, that neurons are constantly emitting electrical impulses.

The brain cells carry the imagery, and this is the basis of your imaginative faculty. Your brain possesses the capacity to reflect on these images, to calculate on the basis of the images, and to make predictions based on them, in a process we know as abstract reasoning.

The object of your formal schooling was (or is) not only to program the organ of your imagination (your brain) with images from the several disciplines we call knowledge, so that you may be considered "educated," but also to lead to a *conditioned reflex* (by a method discovered by Pavlov).

A conditioned reflex is a trained response that has become *autonomic,* which means that it is part of the portion of your imaginative faculty that presents its imagery without conscious control. An example of such conditioning, taken from your elementary schooling, is your automatic response to the basic multiplication table. You don't have to think consciously to find the result of multiplying five and five. You know the result is 25 automatically.

Such conditioning (programming) is also true of all the studies you may have undertaken. If you had been conscientious in your reading and if you had sufficient interest in the subject, then by the act of such reading, you programmed your subconscious with imagery. This now enables you to consciously recall the imagery as needed.

I have been using the expressions *conscious* and *subconscious;* it is important that we understand the difference. The "conscious mind" is that characteristic of your brain function which includes your perceptions, your five senses: sight, hearing, taste, smell, and touch. These are the faculties that enable you to perceive your environment, to be aware.

The conditioning (programming), the storing of information (knowledge), that was mentioned earlier, takes place in the area of your brain that is designated subconscious. You have seen a picture of an iceberg, with its small cap showing above the water and the vast bulk of it below. Here you have a perfect analogy of the relative areas devoted to each function.

Now let us examine what goes on in the minds of two persons who are concentrating. One is a trained, disciplined student who is emotionally mature (free of any hangups). The other has a hangup. The first student is able to concentrate by limiting the imagery in his mind to those images that are related to the thought problem. The second student tries to do the same. However, his imagery is uncontrolled, in that he is unable to restrict the imagery that presents itself, related as well as nonrelated. Soon the nonrelated imagery takes over and his mind is gripped by reverie. Reverie is a pleasant escapist means of avoiding unpleasant imagery, which, in this instance, stemmed from his early traumas. The early traumas are the cause of his feeling of inferiority.

The chances are that the student with the hangup has a well-programmed self-image of inferiority, probably based on early feelings of rejection. He has come to feel unworthy. His self-image is a failure-image, and when he is concentrating, this image intrudes. The result is that his imaginative faculty becomes uncontrolled. In attempting to avoid the painful failure image, he slips into a reverie – a wish-fulfilling daydream – and he loses his concentration.

The solution is obviously for the second student to resolve his failure image by developing a positive success self-image and to train himself to the discipline of concentration.

This is an ancient Chinese philosophic symbol, the Yin/Yang symbol. It represents the male and the female – and the negative and the positive influences, the interaction of which influences the destiny of the individual.

It is therefore singularly appropriate as a means of focusing your mind, of training your imagination to respond to that control we call *concentration.*

It is impossible to think of nothing. Your mind is constantly being bombarded with imagery. The imagery of the person who is free of hangups is usually related to whatever action is being contemplated. It could be pleasant or unpleasant depending on previous experiences relating to the kind of action contemplated. But the imagery is consistent; it is not uncontrolled and therefore does not try to mask or alter the facts in hand, as in a reverie in which a person attempts to repress reality and substitute fantasy.

The person with a hangup usually entertains imagery that can lead to reverie, to avoid the unpleasantness of the imagery that is constantly bubbling up.

The first exercise is a relaxation exercise, because the tensions caused by unpleasant imagery must first be overcome. This exercise will train you not only to control the flow of imagery but to develop your graphic visualization.

The Concentration/Relaxation Exercise

1] Place the Yin/Yang symbol in line with your vision as you sit in a straight-backed chair, hands in your lap loosely, feet flat on the floor.

2] Stare at the symbol. To reject any imagery that may intrude, simply allow your eyes to follow the curves and the symmetry of the male and female symbols. Do not blink but instead stare fixedly until your eyes smart and you are *forced* to blink. Then close your eyes and visualize the complete symbol with your mind's eye. You may not be able to visualize it clearly the first time. Repeat over and over. Each time you open your eyes, stare only at the symbol (do not permit your eyes to wander) until your eyes smart. Close them and visualize. Eventually the image will remain for more than a fleeting moment. In time it will remain as long as your mind concentrates on it.

3] When the image of the symbol is seen with your mind's eye, utter the word "peace" silently, in your thoughts. As long as the image remains repeat the word "peace." Repeat the word slowly, drowsily – feeling more and more relaxed.

4] The moment the image fades from your visualization (this may be as graphic as a photograph or simply your mental interpretation), open your eyes and stare fixedly at the symbol until your eyes smart. Don't allow your eyes to wander. Close your eyes and repeat: "peace . . . peace . . . peace." (Should a foreign image intrude at any time, instantly open your eyes and stare at the symbol. Control your thoughts by contemplating the details of the symbol and the beauty of the curving design.

As with any other exercise, you will develop more and more control. If you have never attempted to control your imaginative faculty before, you will find yourself struggling with vagrant imagery that is attempting to intrude. The great value of this simple exercise, however, is that you are in effect strengthening the "muscles" of your imaginative faculty to the end that you will soon be able to discipline the flow of imagery, which is really all that concentration requires! The following instructions carry forward the primary training to bring you into a completely relaxed state – physically and mentally.

Muscular Repose

5] Change your position from the chair to lying on the floor. Now visualize, with your eyes closed, first your big toe on your right foot. Try to picture it clearly in your mind's eye. Wiggle your toe as you lie there. Try, also, to "see" your toe wiggling.

6] Next visualize your whole foot. Then both of your feet. Gradually allow your legs to enter your image. When you are visualizing both legs up to the knees, utter silently, "Relax!" Then see them slump and collapse as though they were legs of a rag doll.

7] Continue in exactly the same manner to your thighs. Say to yourself, silently, "*Relax.*" Not only will you see them but you will feel them slump. Then on to your torso. See your stomach, your chest, your arms slump – feel the tension seep out of every part of you.

8] Finally visualize your neck and head, particularly your jaw (see it slump open), then visualize your whole body . . . limp, soft, flaccid, totally relaxed.

If at any time a vagrant thought tries to interpose itself, open your eyes immediately and stare down the length of your body, fixing the image of yourself lying there on the floor. Fix the image of your body in your mind's eye as you close your eyes again, then utter: "peace . . . peace . . . peace . . ." silently.

This exercise will accomplish several things. First, it will sharpen your graphic visualization; second, it will train you to control the free flow of imagery; and third, it will relieve you of all physical and mental tension – which is really the reason why you have trouble concentrating.

Chapter 6

How to Meditate and Remember Your Childhood Experiences

IN THIS BOOK you will learn NovaYoga meditation, meditative relaxation, and mantra meditation. Each has a different objective. Meditation is simply an extension of concentration. In Chapter 5 you learned how to control the flow of imagery that is constantly bubbling up within your imaginative faculty. By constantly forcing yourself to visualize the black-and-white symbol of the Yin/Yang you succeeded in strengthening the "muscles" of your imaginative faculty, which are needed to hold back the flow of intruding imagery.

In applying ourselves to the meditative phase of concentration we are still faced with the problem of controlling the flow of imagery. However, we learned that when you find yourself unable to concentrate, it is due to the simple fact that other imagery has taken over to distract your attention, and you follow this imagery (actually because it is usually wish-fulfilling and escapist reverie) and thereby lose your concentration.

Everyone has problems with concentration – the person without hangups as well as the person with. However, the person without hangups finds it difficult to concentrate for a different reason. The subject of his concentration may be something in which he has absolutely no interest, or he may have an actual aversion to it. In that case, he has to exercise more discipline and follow the procedure given in Chapter 5.

The person *with* a hangup, whether the subject of his concentration is interesting or not, may find his concentration wavering and finally lost due to an entirely autogenous reason. This means that his inability to concentrate is due to some deepseated factor in his subconscious. The causal factor may be (and frequently is) a negative self-image which has him failing because as a child he was exposed to experiences that made him feel rejected, inadequate, inferior, or unworthy – any one or all of which result in the creation of that negative self-image, and as we know, "as a man thinketh in his heart, so is he."

Now here he is trying to study. Study calls for concentration. The moment he starts to really concentrate he finds his mind flooded with conflicting imagery, so that, like the grasshopper, he follows the image that is most pleasing (because it is probably wish-fulfilling).

Obviously he will be able to concentrate only when he has overcome his negative self-image and replaced it with a positive self-image. Meanwhile, however, because of his motivation, he will be able to concentrate well enough for the purposes of his NovaYoga practices. He will now have a truly powerful desire to concentrate – because I offer him the opportunity (which has never been offered to him before) of overcoming all his personality problems if he practices these exercises conscientiously. It may mean an extra struggle, greater effort, but look at the reward: to become the person you want to be.

In practicing concentration, you were learning how to restrict *all* imagery other than the Yin/Yang (your symbol of peace). In practicing meditation, however, you are going to learn a system of restricting imagery that is not directly related to the primary image on which you are meditating. This is a *controlled free-association.* The objective of this training is *introspection.*

Here is an example of introspective meditation: concentrating on the Yin/Yang as your symbol of peace, utter silently: "I am at peace, fully relaxed." Gradually you change the image to your tenth birthday (because you have some conscious recollection to enable you to establish the image). You see yourself as you were dressed then in your older brother's hand-me-down suit. The trouble is, by the time you got it, you grew faster than your older brother did when he was ten, so the clothes were too small and tight. You felt self-conscious because of them and you looked down at your feet. You were wearing sneakers, which your mother got from that nice lady next door. But you notice that one sneaker is untied. You see yourself tying it and suddenly your imagery changes.

You now have an image of a girl's sneakers. You see a pretty girl (and this comes from an experience that occurred when you were twelve – two years later) who was wearing sneakers with red-and-white striped ties. Your attention is drawn to the feet of this girl because she is a cheerleader and is kicking her feet high in the air. She is very pretty. You find yourself getting excited watching her. Suddenly she kicks her foot up higher than ever and you see the red-and-white tie . . . and also what you think for a fleeting moment is bare flesh. You feel an erection because you have now visualized her in your fantasy displaying herself in nudity . . . and now your image changes again and you see yourself at home, in the bathroom, masturbating.

This is an example of uncontrolled free association. You can see the associated images, starting with the boy's emotional state (feeling self-conscious, related to his feelings of inferiority) and his focus on his sneakers – with the instant associating image of the girl's sneakers leading finally to his masturbation.

If the object of the introspective meditation was to uncover incidents that contributed to present feelings of guilt, the procedure would have been excellent, for it did reveal an incident that could have been contributory.

But if you are going through introspective meditation to seek incidents relating to, let us say, your present obesity, then such free-association would have to be *controlled* to keep it within the limits you want – that is, related imagery.

Therefore, the moment your imagery slips into another time period and begins to focus on a girl who was a sex stimulus, you must break the free-association. You do this simply by opening your eyes. You may want to investigate this uncovered incident, and you can make a mental note of it. However, you begin again: focus on the Yin/Yang and slip back to the image of yourself as a boy of ten.

Several directions are open to you. You thought of your older brother; you thought of that nice lady next door. Behind these was the ever-present image of your mother. You focus on her in your thoughts and instantly you have an image of the old dining table. You see yourself at one end, with the rest of the table filled with your whole family – all grown, all prodigious eaters, even your next-older brother whose clothes you inherit. You've always looked up to him as your hero. You couldn't identify with anyone else – they were all remote – only your next older brother.

But now in this particular image you suddenly recall how, when the platter was passed to the end of the table your brother swept off what was left, leaving nothing on the platter. You looked at him with all the hurt of a small child, your hero suddenly crumbling and tears starting in your eyes. You don't want anyone to see the tears (although no one pays the slightest attention) and you leave the table. Your mother, who was at the stove, comes into the bedroom and sees you with your face buried in the pillow. She gathers you to her breast and whispers, "Don't cry; wait until they leave." The image changes and you see yourself sitting alone at the table with a plate piled high with all the leavings!

If you are looking for a suitable causal factor for your present obesity, you've found it. Here is an image of early conditioning related to eating. Not only did it condition you to stuff yourself, but that leftover food that was piled high on your plate became – to you – a symbol of love, from the only person during your developing years who demonstrated love.

Introspective Meditation

1] Sit in a comfortable chair so arranged that the Yin/Yang symbol can be propped up in your line of vision. Stare at the symbol until your eyes begin to smart. Close your eyes, visualize the symbol, utter silently "I am at peace – fully relaxed."

2] You will find yourself relaxing more and more as you dwell mentally on the Yin/Yang symbol. (As in the example quoted above, you will have chosen some particular period in your early life as a starting point because you do have some conscious recall with a suggestion of an emotional experience.)

3] You are concentrating on the Yin/Yang (this will become your symbol for peace, a form of concentration that will result in physical and mental relaxation). When you are relaxed, you will find the symbol fading. Let it go. In its place visualize the incident you had decided on. See yourself as clearly as you

can by trying to feel the emotion you felt at that time and that place. You will stimulate recall by mentally prodding yourself with questions.

4] Example: "I am eleven years old. I remember this day clearly. We all came home from school and Joey and I were arguing. Joey is my friend who lives next door. He's smaller than me. He's always trying to better me. All our friends are there. Frankie starts to push me from behind, saying, 'Go on, fight him, fight him!' I don't want to fight Joey. He's my friend. But then Joey makes a fist and swings at me hitting me in the chest. I fall back a step and Frankie pushes me again, 'Fight him, fight him!' Joey is holding his fists like a prizefighter. I am bigger than him, so I suppose I could lick him. But I turn away and Frankie starts to yell, 'You're afraid of him . . . you're afraid of him 'n he's littler than you!' I push Frankie away and then I put my arm around Joey's shoulders and we walk away."

5] This was the incident that has been bugging you, evidently because it is the first that presents itself to you for introspection. The image of you leading Joey away is now in your mind, and this thought comes crashing through: "I really *was* afraid to fight Joey! I really was afraid of him!"

This is introspective meditation. You relax yourself by use of the Yin/Yang symbol and then bring to mind the imagery relating to some incident that suggests itself to you. It may be (and probably usually is) vague, but something about that experience is unresolved. Otherwise it would not be sufficiently important to suggest itself.

The object of your introspective session is to explore that incident, endeavor to reexperience the emotions you have repressed somehow. As in the example (you recall the incident) and then by review, you are suddenly shocked by the hidden emotion; you feel you have acted cowardly.

Apparently that was the case. However, it isn't of such monumental importance as to continue bugging you – now – or is it? Let's go back to the meditation:

6] You repeat the procedure: stare at the Yin/Yang symbol until you are relaxed. Allow the image to fade and recall the image of you and Joey. As you walk away with him you are saying, "I don't want to fight you, you're my friend." Joey shrugs your arm off his shoulder and sneers up at you: "Yeah? I can lick you anytime!" You separate because you have come to your house. Joey's is next door.

7] As you walk up the steps you suddenly realize your heart has been pounding, and now Joey's rejoinder starts it fluttering. "It's true! I *am* afraid to fight him." You feel like crying but you check yourself and go into your room. You see yourself lying on your bed, red-faced, and this thought suddenly comes crashing through: Joey shrugged off your arm around his shoulder . . . he hates me . . . and I love him . . . you suddenly realize that the whole incident meant nothing about your cowardice . . . nothing . . . so why do I have to be so aggressive, so domineering, so possessive – *now*? The meaning becomes clear to you. You realize now that that aspect of the incident which you had repressed was *not* the feeling that you were a coward, and therefore, that *now* your hangup was expressed as a domineering, belligerent, extremely virile one. It suddenly becomes very clear: you have been fighting the accusation that you are homosexual!

Not all introspective meditation will be as revealing as the example above. It may take time and many trials before the *emotional* experiences are thoroughly understood. As in the example, the man had a hangup. It was demonstrated by his extreme aggressiveness and his constant effort to prove his masculinity, his virility. He was always chasing chicks. He had earned a reputation as a powerful lay. The fact was, however, that he never dated a girl more than once, because the first time was enough to prove that he was not the virile person he tried to make himself to be. His problem was sexual impotency. He had been rejecting the idea that he could be homosexual.

At 11, 12, and 13 most boys do indeed have homosexual tendencies and, sometimes, experiences. However, in the normal course of their development their interest in sexual experimentation turns away from others of their own sex to the opposite sex. In the case of this young man his impotency was overcome when he realized this as a biological fact of life, and that he had no basis for blaming himself for his feelings toward Joey. Rationalizing the incident enabled him to mentally thank Joey for shrugging his arm off his shoulders! He was able to pursue heterosexual experiences thereafter satisfactorily.

Controlling Free-Association Imagery

The examples noted in the technique of introspective meditation demonstrate the manner of your control of the imagery that presents itself to your mind when you are in the *relaxed* state of consciousness. It is of primary importance that you practice the concentration on the Yin/Yang symbol until you are able to slip readily into the relaxed state.

Controlling free association, as demonstrated in the examples quoted, is the object of training yourself in this introspective-meditation technique. Related free-association images are those images which relate to the present symptom, to that personality mannerism you now wish to overcome. Assuming that your present symptom is obesity (and you do not have the slightest idea why you are a compulsive eater), your introspective search for the causal factor is an examination of your earliest experiences that could possibly have this implication. The distinction between the associative image of the sneakers and the associative image of the mother is a case in point. One led to a sexually stimulating experience, while the other led directly to an experience that held the causal factor.

1] Seek a place for your meditation practice that is quiet, free of disturbing influences, that is, other persons, pets, telephone, excessive noise.
2] Always seat yourself in a comfortable chair – but one that is not so comfortable that you are liable to fall asleep in it! Position the book, open to the page on which the Yin/Yang symbol appears, so that you can stare at it without strain.
3] Stare at the Yin/Yang symbol until your eyes begin to smart. Close your eyes and hold the image in your mind's eye while you utter silently: "I am at peace, fully relaxed," feeling yourself going into muscular repose . . . let yourself drift . . . drift into total relaxation.
4] As the image of the Yin/Yang begins to fade, replace it with whatever imagery you have chosen (this is imagery relating to any earlier period in your life of which you have some conscious recall, as in the examples quoted).
5] The image will begin to reveal whatever emotional content may have significance – by silent mental prodding. (All thinking is actually talking to oneself!) As you think back to this incident, review it silently, as though you were relating it to another. You will

find that the repressed portions of this "forgotten" imagery will begin to reveal themselves.

6] At some point in your introspection you will perceive an intruding image (this may be a genuine free-association image). Allow it to develop. If it is not (and you will know immediately whether it is or is not because of its emotional content), you can void it by opening your eyes.

7] Upon opening your eyes you break the sequence of imagery. You will now repeat the procedure, staring at the Yin/Yang, etc., and repeat the recalling of the incident. Again, as you "talk" to yourself about this incident, other imagery will intrude. Genuine free-association imagery will develop eventually.

8] Allow yourself to pursue the free-associating imagery. Remember: the process is maintained by "talking" to yourself. "I remember how, etc., etc."

9] Eventually (although this may take much time, trial, and practice) you will uncover material that probably was causative because of its traumatic content.

10] When such material is uncovered, it must be rationalized. Review "rationalization" and follow the procedure outlined there.

Summary

This is important practice, because you are learning how to direct and control the awesome power of your imagination.

Introspection stems from the school of analytical psychology. This school holds that your present personality pattern is the result of early conditioning experiences and that traumatic experiences (often repressed) can create specific personality characteristics which inhibit the free expression of your id and ego. Uncovering these early experiences and rationalizing them is considered cathartic. You "wash out" the influence, in effect, by such rationalization and are thereby free to become mature, to become the person you want to be.

However, there is an opposing school of psychology which holds that your personality pattern is your *behavior* pattern, that by modifying, or, in effect, altering your present behavior pattern, you are effectively dealing with the causative factor. An example of this is the reconditioning of a person's *fear*. You have a fear of dogs, let us assume, and you wish to overcome this fear since it inhibits you in your relation to your girl friend who adores dogs.

The behavioristic procedure is to relax you by means of projected pictures of a dog – first seen at a great distance and then closer and closer with each succeeding session, so that eventually the dog is at hand, at which point a perfectly lovable, tame dog is introduced (live) for touching and petting. When you have been exposed to this succession of exposures – with your ability in the final session to actually pat a dog – you have effectively overcome your behavior pattern.

NovaYoga recognizes the value of either procedure.

Chapter 7

How to Experience the Alpha Rhythm with Meditative Relaxation

IN CLASSIC YOGA the world of your reality lies within you, not without. The world of your physical environment is delusion, for did not St. Paul state: "The Kingdom of God is within you"?

Philosophers still ponder the question: If a tree were to fall with no person to witness the falling, did it fall in reality or does it require conscious recognition to make it so? In other words, what constitutes reality?

Over the millennia of man's struggle to rise from the ooze of this emerging planet, one fact has made possible the earth as we know it. It is that, as life forms developed and proliferated in all directions – from the earliest amoeba of the Precambrian era to the invertebrates of the Cambrian period and to the amphibians, reptiles, and insects that appeared in the late Paleozoic era to the present life forms including insects, fishes, amphibians, birds, reptiles, and mammals – man evolved to become the dominant species.

Why?

Because man, as he evolved, developed that mental attribute we know as the *imaginative faculty.* No other life form on this planet possesses this faculty. It is essential to creation and to abstract concepts. We apply this imaginative faculty to the concept of "God," for Genesis should read ". . . and man created God in his own image"!

NovaYoga meditative relaxation employs the imaginative faculty in conditioning your mind to attain that altered state of consciousness which connotes complete freedom from tension, mental and physical.

Imagination, the Basis of Faith and Belief

> "And behold, a woman who was diseased with an issue of blood for twelve years, came behind him and touched the hem of his garment. 'For,' she said within herself, 'if I but touch his garment, I shall be whole.'
>
> "But Jesus turned about and seeing the woman said, 'Woman dost thou believe that I can cure thee?'
>
> "And the woman replied, 'Yea, Lord!'
>
> "And Jesus said, 'Daughter, be of good comfort, thy faith hath made thee whole!'
>
> "And the woman was made whole from that hour."

Nowhere in the Bible does it state that Jesus ever claimed that *he* cured anyone. But every instance of a cure is explained by Jesus' statement: "Thy faith hath cured thee." It is not recorded that he ever said, "I cured you" or "God cured you." It is always, "Do you believe?" and "Your faith hath cured. . . ."

Let us examine the psychodynamics of faith and belief so that we may understand what part this plays in attaining the total benefits of meditative relaxation.

A classic example of psychosomatic illness is the stomach ulcer. Your medical doctor will confirm this, because his usual procedure is to urge his patient to stop worrying, put him on a bland diet to help counteract the hyperacidity that is ulcerating his stomach, give him a sedative to help calm his nerves – in an effort to relieve his patient's tensions.

Analyzing the dynamics, we learn that the patient is a chronic worrier. Worry is a function of the mind that begins with the creation of *conscious negation,* which in turn creates a subconscious negative self-image. Something in this person's environment is posing an apparent threat to his feelings of security. He reacts to it subliminally, and then, probably because of early negative conditioning, his imaginative faculty dwells on all the negative aspects in the situation. In short, it begins with his *conscious* worry, and this, in turn, leads to subliminal tension, which eventually causes the ulcer. This analysis is oversimplified, but it is the essence of the problem.

Your subconscious does not exercise volition. It is not capable of inductive reasoning and therefore cannot censor and reject negative suggestions that filter down from your conscious mind. The best analogy has been made by Dr. Maxwell Malz, who said the subconscious is a computer-mechanism that is constantly being programmed by the conscious mind. All the thoughts, ideas, experiences, and emotions – negative or positive – are implanted in your subconscious computer by the programming, perceptive area of your mind.

How often have you heard someone say, "Oh, I've got a lousy memory"? This is said in a moment of pique when someone tries to force quick recall of something that may be of relatively little interest and hence made little impression in your memory bank. But you may be certain that this person is assuring himself of a "lousy" memory. When you keep telling yourself that you have a poor memory, you are actually conditioning your subconscious computer to provide you with a truly poor memory.

Your subconcious may be conditioned to make you ill; it can just as easily be conditioned to make you well.

The person who has *faith* in himself has little fear that he will ever develop a stomach ulcer.

Consider the hundreds of persons who come regularly to the grotto where Our Lady of Lourdes is said to have appeared to St. Bernadette in 1858. Over a million pilgrims a year visit this shrine in southwestern France. The sick, the maimed, those eager for a dip into the healing waters of the sacred grotto are first examined by the priests. If the sufferer appears to have sufficient faith and belief, he is permitted to enter the water. It is a matter of record that a small number do leave the water crying, "I am cured, I am cured!"

Could it be the water? It has been examined and chemically analyzed and found to contain nothing which could even remotely be considered a curative or medicinal agent. What, then, brings about these seemingly miraculous cures?

Jesus said, ". . . faith . . . belief. . . ."

Faith and belief are actual powers resulting from the positive imagery created within your imaginative faculty. They have been the subject of many books on the power of positive thinking. The power stems from the psychosomatic, as well as the somatopsychic effects that NovaYoga training is designed to enable you to use and control, that is: the reconditioning of your negative self-image to the positive self-image of the person you want to be.

It is because your study and application to NovaYoga will lead to your reconditioning imagery that it is important for you to understand why, as well as how, to use the power of faith and belief in learning the technique of meditative relaxation in order to let yourself go.

To Let Yourself Go

To let yourself go is simply to suspend the critical faculty of your conscious mind, thereby accepting the suggestions that are intended to do you good. Alfred Adler once remarked of such procedures: "All that is necessary is that you obey . . . [then magic happens]!" This is where your faith and belief take over.

Example: when you consult your medical doctor, the aura of his exalted status, which our society invests in him, speedily enables you to establish rapport. Everything he tells you, everything he prescribes for you, everything he pronounces, you accept with total faith and belief. He knows this and he employs this power (actually bolstering his omniscience by telling you nothing) to help you to become the well person you want to be.

So, too, it is important that a feeling of rapport be established between you and me, so that you can accept everything I tell you without fear, without resistance, and without analysis. You will thereby be able to truly let yourself go, and when you do, a kind of magic begins to happen.

The first evidence of this "magic" is that you will lose all your tensions. Today there are hundreds of "meditation centers" springing up for the avowed purpose of training persons to overcome their tensions. In our modern society tension has become an ugly fact of life. Witness our drug problem, our crime problem, our ethnic problem, problems almost without end, and every one caused by tension.

You, too, have tension. Why else would you be studying NovaYoga? Fortunately, NovaYoga goes far beyond merely reducing your tension, because this is merely the first step toward training you to overcome all your personality problems (which cause your tension). And you will speedily overcome your tensions by exercising the power of your faith and belief – as you learn to employ that awesome power that lies within your imaginative faculty.

How to Attain Faith and Belief

First, there must be rapport. You and I will attain this rapport as you read this book, especially when you reach Part Two and learn how I developed this autogenic procedure in order to overcome my own personality problem.

Second, you will be able to review a number of case histories of persons who, like yourself, had some vexing or inhibiting hangups that were preventing them from attaining their goals.

Third, once you begin to apply the exercises and follow the directions of the several procedures, you will become alert to recognizing your small successes. These are evidences that changes are actually taking place, such as being able to do something you had never had the courage to attempt before (you'll read about my first small success in Chapter 13).

As you begin to add one small success to another small success – and another and another – you will eventually reach a state of *conviction*. And when you reach the state of conviction, you will have overcome your problem – forever!

Here, in review, are small successes you will begin to experience (indeed may have already experienced!).

Starting with the hathayoga exercises: if you practice regularly, I have absolutely no doubt that you will soon feel a keener sense of physical well-being – small success number 1.

If you perform the breathing exercises properly and regularly, there can be no other result than a sense of improved mental acuity – small success number 2.

Practice and training in concentration will bolster your feeling of power because of your new ability to keep your mind from drifting into reverie by repressing intruding imagery – small success number 3.

As you begin to apply your training in concentration to the meditation procedure, you will learn to relax and free yourself of tension, and you will be able to go into early recall and introspection – small success number 4.

You will soon have the faith of a mustard seed!

The Meditative Relaxation Procedure

The meditative relaxation procedure is formalized. It follows a set pattern to enable you, with repeated practice, to attain a conditioned reflex. When you are able to attain complete relaxation, both physically and mentally, you may begin training yourself to a shorter procedure (the flash technique), which will release your tensions instantly.

While meditative relaxation may be practiced at any time and at almost any place, it is best done in bed, just before sleep, in a quiet, darkened room protected against the possible intrusion of pets, children, or noise.

But what about married couples sleeping in double beds? Inasmuch as the entire procedure is mental, actually all that is needed is simply to put out the light, kiss your mate "good night," curl up on your side – and begin the mental procedure. In my practice, I provide a cassette tape which is listened to by means of an earphone, so that my voice continues to train the subject.

The procedure employs symbology which possesses universal emotional appeal. A complete explanation of the symbolistic effect will be given in a later chapter. Here it is necessary that the symbology of the relaxation image employed as part of the technique be understood. Water is the most ancient relaxation symbol because man is eternally drawn to his origins. You will be trained to an image of yourself lying on a blanket on a beach close to the water. If you are unfamiliar with an ocean beach scene, you may employ a lake or river scene – whichever is within your experience.

The formalized procedure is in three steps: (1) the cue, to alert your subconscious; (2) the breaths, to alert your brain with increased oxygen; and (3) muscular repose, to relax every nerve, every muscle, every cell and tissue, after which you will learn to *let yourself go.* When you do, you will experience the alpha rhythm.

You can practice in a straight-backed chair with your feet flat on the floor and your hands lying limp in your lap. Or you may lie on the floor (as in hathayoga muscular repose) or on your bed. When you are composed, close your eyes and do this:

THE CUE:

> Say to yourself silently in your thoughts, while visualizing the Yin/Yang image: "I am at peace . . . fully relaxed." Think and talk to yourself drowsily.

THE BREATHS:

> Say to yourself silently in your thoughts: "With each breath I take, I am going to let myself go . . . into deep, deep relaxation." Inhale deeply (diaphragmatically) as you count silently to eight, then hold your breath as you count silently to four. Release your breath vigorously, compressing the muscles of your diaphragm so that your breath is expelled with "hu-uh!" Inhale again very deeply as you count to eight. Hold your breath as you count to four. Release your breath vigorously – "hu-uh!" Inhale for the third time as you count to eight. Hold your breath as you count to four. Release your breath – "hu-uh!"

MUSCULAR REPOSE:

Visualize every part of your body – and
actually feel each muscle going soft and limp as
you mention it. Say to yourself, silently:
"I feel a sensation of relaxation at the bottom of my
feet – I feel it so plainly – From my toes to my
heels, washing out all tension –
I feel the relaxation
now, passing through my ankles –
Up my calves to my knees, washing out all tension –
So that now, every nerve, every muscle, in my calves
is soft, limp, free of all tension –
I feel it now passing through my knees up my thighs –
to my hips, washing out all tension –
So that now, every nerve, every muscle in my thighs
is soft, limp, free of all tension –
I feel it now, passing through my hips, up my back to
my shoulders, down my arms to my wrists, my hands,
my fingers, washing out all tension –
So that now, every nerve, every muscle in my back,
my arms, my wrists, my hands, my fingers, is soft,
limp, free of all tension –
I feel it now in my neck, traveling over my skull to my
forehead, my face, my jaw, my throat, washing out all
tension –
So that now, every nerve, every muscle in my neck,
my skull, my forehead, my face, my jaw, my throat, is
soft, limp, free of all tension –
I feel it now in my chest, traveling down to my
abdomen and throughout all the organs in my body,
washing out all tension –
So that now, every nerve, every muscle, every cell and
tissue of my body is completely free of all tension –
I have never felt more relaxed than I do at this
moment."

RELAXATION IMAGE:

> At this moment, you will create your relaxation image. See yourself in your mind's eye lying on a blanket, under an umbrella to protect you from the sun. You are dressed in a bathing suit. Every nerve and muscle in your body is completely relaxed. Your jaw muscles are unclenched, your mouth hangs open, your arms limp and loose, your legs all soft and rubbery – your whole body so flaccid that you would roll off your bed or your chair if given a shove, because there is no tension in any of your muscles to hold you. As you conjure up this image of yourself completely relaxed, listening to the waves and the sounds of the seagulls in the distance, you will let yourself go, by *drifting into a passive reverie.* Don't think, don't concentrate, let your reverie take you into peace.

ALPHA RHYTHM:

> You will experience the euphoria of the alpha rhythm as you learn to *let yourself go in a passive reverie.* (In my office I employ a brain wave analyzer with the electrodes attached to the occipital lobe and your temple to report the emission of alpha – as you let yourself go.)

Your Success Image and Positive Suggestions

When you have trained yourself to reach this altered state of consciousness (characterized by total freedom from tension) you will create your success image. (Detailed instructions will be given in Chapter 12.)

This image will always be accompanied by the

positive, reinforcing suggestions. After these suggestions are repeated three times you will then say to yourself: "I will drift now – into a deep, normal, natural, physiological sleep. I will sleep the whole night through and awake alert, refreshed, completely relaxed, and this thought will flash through my mind: "Every day in every way I am better and better."

Your Personal Relaxation Image

If you are perfectly comfortable with the symbolic relaxation image [the beach scene] then you need not pursue the following explanation. Occasionally however, someone is not at perfect ease with the image of the beach. In that case it is important that you choose your *personal* relaxation image. This is a conscious recall of a happy experience in childhood, or any later time when you were completely free of anxiety, worry, or responsibility of any kind. This must not be synthetic, that is, made up from your imagination, but an actual happy recollection of yourself being completely relaxed.

Such a personal relaxation image is best when you are emotionally involved. One of the best examples we can quote is the relaxation image chosen by a young woman who came to me for help with her insomnia. When I asked her to recall some very pleasant incident out of her past which she could employ as her personal relaxation image she exclaimed, "Oh, I simply cannot remember ever being completely relaxed or ever free of tension and worry!" It took two sessions to prove that she was wrong, because as she practiced Meditation she let herself slip backward in time through introspection and this is the image she produced:

She saw herself, as a child of seven, being called by her mother. She saw the house in which she was born, with its weathered off-white clapboard siding and jonquil yellow shutters, with her mother beckoning from the doorway. She was led up the stairs to her bedroom and here her mother slipped her dress over her head. She kicked off her shoes and climbed into her bed. She had been ill and now it was time for her afternoon nap. In bed she stretched out her arms and her mother dropped a pink teddybear into them. She clutched her teddybear security blanket and with a completely relaxed sigh, slipped into sleep.

This personal relaxation image was, for her, the most powerful relaxation image possible! She was trained to use this image in bed every night, in place of sleeping pills, and for her the result was magical.

Most personal relaxation images will be found in some pleasant and nostalgic experience from childhood – although the actual mental imagery can be something within the adult present. An excellent example of this came from another young woman who was recently married. She decided on her personal relaxation image other than the beach scene because she came from the mid-West and had no reminiscence of relaxing on a beach. She pictured herself curled up, in the evening, on the couch in her living room – with her husband reading the paper at the other end of the couch.

When she was questioned about this somewhat odd image she said, "All I can say is that that image flashed into my mind when you spoke of an alternate personal relaxation image. It was a 'natural.' It made me feel completely loved, secure, relaxed – with my husband sitting so my feet touched him. But, when I practiced introspection in Meditation the image of myself as a little girl popped right into my mind! I had completely forgotten about it! But there I was curled up in one corner of our old couch and my daddy was sitting in the other corner reading the paper. He would reach out, while reading, and pat my ankle . . . while I purred like a pussycat!"

The important aspect of any relaxation image, whether it be the symbolic beach scene or your very own personal relaxation image, is your emotional involvement. You've got to feel the peace, the relaxation, the drifting off into hypnagogic sleep. Whichever image you choose, be sure to practice with it until you can, indeed, drift off into that altered state of consciousness wherein you can – let yourself go!

The Flash Technique

Once you have conditioned yourself to the complete meditative relaxation procedure, attained complete relaxation (freedom from all tension), you will be ready to learn an instantaneous technique.

The slow, deliberate, formalized procedure is most effective when it is performed directly before sleep. Inasmuch as it is a procedure which releases your tension (and prepares you to receive and accept autosuggestions), it need not be limited to night-time use. There will be many occasions when you will have need of an instantaneous relaxation technique to relieve you of anxiety tensions caused by some unexpected situation.

Suppose you have attended a gathering of some sort at which you did not expect to speak, and you are suddenly called on (perhaps because you may be considered expert in some area of discussion) and you experience sudden panic. This anxiety panic can be relieved instantaneously when you have conditioned yourself with the flash technique.

It is necessary, however, to give this word of caution: you *must* condition yourself first with the complete, formalized technique. Only after you have been so conditioned will you be ready for conditioning with the flash technique.

It is suggested that you practice the flash technique every morning directly after you have completed your morning ablutions. Before leaving the bathroom, lower the cover seat of the toilet bowl, sit on it with both feet flat on the floor, hands limp in your lap.

1] Close your eyes and visualize the Yin/Yang symbol. Say to yourself silently: "I am at peace – fully relaxed." You will feel yourself going limp.
2] Continue silently: "From the tips of my toes to the top of my head, every nerve, every muscle, every cell and tissue in my body, is completely free of all tension – I have *never* felt more relaxed than I do at this moment."
3] You will give yourself the suggestions to overcome the stress-producing situation: "I am happy to speak to this meeting, I am happy to speak to this meeting."

This is all. You will be free of tension and you will indeed be happy to speak to this meeting. A couple of weeks of such practice will enable you to use this technique in a situation as described. It takes only a few seconds – and you will be able to release all your tensions before you leave your seat to walk to the podium.

Meditative Relaxation for Serenity

You began to train yourself to attain serenity when you practiced concentration, visualizing the Yin/Yang symbol, saying to yourself, silently, "I am at peace . . . fully relaxed . . . I am at peace. . . ."

If you continued with your practice in meditative relaxation and have practiced concentration and meditation, you should now be able to relieve yourself of all tension. Continued practice in meditative relaxation will establish your conditioned reflex, giving you that constant feeling of serenity.

Biofeedback to Overcome Migraine Headache

The term "biofeedback" is best defined by giving an example. Actually, you began to train yourself via biofeedback from the moment you were born. It is part of the programming that is going on in your brain every moment of your life. For example, as an infant you had to learn coordination. You reached out to grab an object. The first thing your brain had to learn was to reach in the right direction and then to open the fingers, close them about the object, and then return your hand to your mouth. The whole process, which appears so elementary to you now, was a phenomenal achievement then.

The training you are undergoing now in meditation and meditative relaxation is training in biofeedback. You are learning how to overcome tensions, and you accomplish this by means of your imaginative faculty. So, too, you will now train yourself to use your imagination to overcome migraine, and in the process, hypertension.

A migraine headache is caused by an excessive flow of blood into the brain. The pituitary gland, which is located almost in the very center of your head, is protected by a cradle of bone. When there is an excess of blood, this gland has no place to expand and the pressure therefore causes excruciating pain. Biofeedback training to control the flow of blood from your brain to your hands relieves the pressure and hence the pain.

If you are a migraine sufferer I know you will devote the time required to train yourself. It needn't be long – only as long as you can learn to let yourself go in meditative relaxation. Then practice this flash technique:

When you feel the onset of a migraine headache, sit in a comfortable easy chair, close your eyes, visualize the Yin/Yang and say to yourself silently: "I am at peace . . . fully relaxed . . . I am at peace . . . fully relaxed. . . ."

Then exercise your imagination. See your head, try to visualize your brain, see it *red,* full of blood, then, by the power of your imagination, *see* it fade . . . become pale . . . at that instant, *see* your hands become *red, feel* your hands becoming hot and red. . . .

Then say to yourself silently: "the blood in my brain is flowing into my hands . . . the blood in my brain is flowing into my hands . . . I can feel my hands becoming *hot . . . hot . . . hot.* The blood is flowing from my brain into my hands. . . ."

Concentrate your thoughts and your imaginative faculty on your hands. *See* your hands turning red, *feel* your hands becoming hot.

With practice – a week? two weeks? more? – it's up to you. But you may be assured that if you've been conscientious about applying yourself to all the exercises given in this book, both physical and mental, you will find this relatively easy – and a blessing! But if you have difficulty *visualizing* your hands getting hot, try this: cross your arms over your chest so that each hand is tucked under the opposite armpit. In a few moments you will feel them getting *hot* as you silently go through the exercise, with eyes closed, as described above.

A *tension headache,* though different from the migraine in cause, responds to a similar procedure. You follow the same flash technique – but now your visualization is on your neck, on the atlas and axis vertebrae in the neck:

Sitting in a comfortable easy chair, close your eyes, visualize the Yin/Yang, and say to yourself silently:

"I am at peace . . . fully relaxed . . . I am at peace . . . fully relaxed." Then exercise your imagination – *see* your neck . . . imagine your axis and atlas vertebrae pinching the nerve . . . then instantly *feel* your hands *tingle . . . feel* a tingling sensation flow down your arms, into your hands, and through your fingers. Then say to yourself silently: "The tension is flowing from my neck through my hands, leaving me as water pours from a glass . . . the tension is flowing from my fingers like water pouring from a glass. . . ."

Concentrate your thoughts on your hands and fingers. You will soon feel a pins-and-needles sensation.

This is *biofeedback;* it will relieve your tension and your tension headache.

If you have difficulty experiencing that tingle, do this: place both hands palms down on the chair, so that you can sit on them. In a few minutes you'll feel that tingling sensation.

You continued with practice in meditation, which carried forward the relaxation procedure to develop your controlled free-association imagery. Now you have begun your practice of meditative relaxation, which makes use of both concentration and meditation, to enable you to relieve yourself of all tension. Continued practice in meditative relaxation will establish a conditioned reflex, giving you that feeling of serenity, not only during practice but all of the time.

The secret is in learning how to let yourself go.

The procedure itself is fairly easy to memorize. You will become progressively more and more relaxed as you practice. When you reach the conclusion of muscular repose, all that is necessary to condition yourself for serenity is to let yourself drift off with your relaxation image – drift off in a state of *passive reverie,* no longer concentrating, no longer thinking, no longer performing;

simply drift and you will experience the delightful euphoria of the alpha rhythm – for serenity.

Summary

Meditative relaxation is a state of altered consciousness you experience as you enter hypnagogic sleep and you begin to emit the brain wave rhythm designated as alpha (which connotes freedom from tension).

To attain this state the critical faculty of your conscious mind becomes quiescent (characteristic of hypnagogic sleep). This simply means that you are becoming relaxed both physically and mentally. You cannot attain the quiescent state if you remain critical.

If you find yourself unable to attain the relaxed state, begin your practice of meditative relaxation by saying silently: "I am going to let myself go – without fear, without resistance, and without analysis. . . . I am at peace . . . fully relaxed."

Remember Alfred Adler's dictum, "All that is necessary is that you obey. . . ."

Chapter 8

How to Reach Your Center of Tranquility with Astral Projection

IN CLASSIC YOGA the astral body is an ethereal substance having a very high rate of vibration. It is an exact counterpart of the physical body. It is neither matter nor force but is finer and more tenacious than any substance known to science.

As NovaYoga has adapted exercises from hathayoga, layayoga, and mantrayoga, so too does it adapt the concept of the astral body. Since NovaYoga is the yoga of the imagination, however, the concept is limited to the area of the subconscious.

Training in NovaYoga astral projection carries forward the training you have already received – concentration, meditation, and meditative relaxation. These three steps are exercises in the training of your imaginative faculty. They will lead you to the mastery of astral projection, to enable you to attain that altered state of consciousness which brings tranquility.

Symbology

Symbolism is a subtle form of communication. In the area of dreams it has been the subject of extensive research and analysis. Carl Jung discovered universal symbols common to disparate cultures in his studies and research of racial unconscious. Myths, religions, folkways, mores – all have a universal bond of understanding that reaches deeply into the universal psyche.

The symbols employed in NovaYoga astral projection to guide your imaginative faculty toward integration with the absolute power that lies within the center of your being have powerful, fundamental, and deeply emotional significance.

Water is the most ancient relaxation symbol, because man is eternally drawn to his origins. For this reason the relaxation image can place you on a beach, near water.

The bird is a symbol of spirit. A seagull* is employed because it is a water bird, but any bird suitable to your relaxation image (if it is other than an ocean beach) may be employed.

A cloud, which represents the veil that separates the known from the unknown, limiting man to his three-dimensional world, is used because all clouds are made up of moisture.

The sun, which illuminates the cloud, is the symbol of your life force – the energy and the creative power.

The sun's rays, shining through the myriad drops of water within the cloud, are defracted as though by tiny prisms, creating the rainbow of colors. Each color is a vibration, as the entire spectrum of colors is represented scientifically by the angstrom units, a measure of their vibrations. These vibrations are a vital force, employed to strengthen the astral body.

Your inner space is quite different from your outer

---

* To help you with your visualization it is suggested you read the book by Richard Bach, *Jonathan Livingston Seagull.* This bird has learned how to pass through the veil, and inasmuch as such a bird has been employed in NovaYoga astral projection, it would help you with your visualization.

space. As the astronauts discovered, all outer space is darkness. Your inner space, on the contrary, is brilliantly illuminated by the light of the sun's rays – the source of your life's energy. The concept of your inner space is taken from Ernest Dimnet, the Abbé philosopher, and his book, *The Art of Thinking.* You will visualize your inner space as a vaulted chamber, the base of which is a flowing stream of liquid sunshine. It is brilliantly illuminated because of the vibrant energy of the sun. This illumination is known as Christ-light.

The Yin/Yang symbol, used in your concentration exercise, represents the dual distribution of forces, combining the active (masculine) and the passive (feminine) principles. It is a section of the universal whirlwind which brings opposites together and engenders perpetual motion. The entrance to and exit from this motion lie outside, in the same way that life and death lie outside the consciousness of the individual. The vertical axis through the center constitutes the "unvarying mean" or *mystic center,* where there is no rotation, no restlessness, no impulse nor suffering of any kind – only *peace.*

NovaYoga agrees with Jung who asserted in his book, *On Psychic Energy,* that: "The spiritual appears in the psyche as an instinct, indeed as a real passion . . . it is not derived from any other instinct, but is a principle *sui generis,* that is, a specific and necessary form of instinctual power."

The Astral Projection Procedure

NovaYoga astral projection is an extension of the meditative relaxation technique. You begin with your concentration on the Yin/Yang, saying to yourself: "I am at peace . . . fully relaxed."

The three breaths follow, then you proceed with muscular repose. When you have relaxed physically and mentally you will visualize your relaxation image and continue with:

YOUR ASTRAL BODY:

You are now completely quiescent. Your critical faculty is drifting in hypnagogic sleep. You are aware of the sounds of the water as it rolls up the beach and of the sound of the seagulls. One special gull, a large white and gray with black-tipped wings, flies down to the sand and waddles over to your recumbent body lying there on the blanket. It steps daintily on the corner of the blanket in the area of your left shoulder. It does this to interrupt your bodily aura. Everyone, as you know, exudes an electrical charge, and this electrical field is known as the *aura.*

The gull is in the area of your left shoulder and is able to contact that dynamo, the source of your bodily electrical energy, your brain. It does this to enable you to release your astral body, and this you do by allowing your id/ego to materialize. This is made possible only because you are now in deep hypnagogic sleep – experiencing the alpha rhythm. But how do you *materialize* your astral body? You do so by recognizing that your id/ego is you – your personality – that essence of instinctual power, plus your programmed experiences, that is characteristically *you.* All that is required is that you *visualize* yourself, see yourself no taller than three inches! This is the materialization of yourself, your id/ego – no taller than three inches!

See yourself now dressed as your recumbent body, that is, in a bathing suit. See yourself astride the back of the seagull. You are smiling, anticipating a wondrous, a magical, adventure. A tiny jockey on a tiny racehorse. You clutch the feathers of the gull's neck and marvel at the downy softness, but now the gull spreads his wings and in a moment is aloft. It is flying higher and higher, and now faster and faster toward a low-hanging cloud on the horizon.

In a moment the gull enters the cloud and instantly you are aware of the myriad droplets of water and of the brilliant sunshine that is illuminating the cloud. Each drop of water acts as a prism and defracts the sun's rays, so that you are now being bathed in color, every color in the spectrum. These are pure vibrations, and these vibrations strengthen and reinforce your imaginative faculty and all the imagery and all the suggestions to which you are being trained.

The bird flies faster and faster and in a moment is beyond. . . . It has brought you beyond time and space! With training you will lose awareness of your physical environment and become aware of your inner space. You will visualize it as a vaulted chamber, shaped as your skull, with the base an endless stream of liquid sunshine.

The gull rests now while you slip into the stream, floating on your back, being supported, caressed, and loved by that energy, that force, that power which gave you life – for all life on this planet was created and is being supported by the sun. Visualize this as your inner space, surrounded by the brightness of the sun, and you are floating, at peace in this vibrant stream . . . drifting . . . drifting . . . into passive reverie, surrounded by Christ-light. Do not think. Do not concentrate. Let yourself go . . . into passive reverie.

15 MINUTES:

All these exercises are designed for 15-minute periods. To set your "mental clock" you may begin each session with, "I am going to let myself go into deep relaxation for 15 minutes – 15 minutes – after which

I will arouse fully alert, smiling, and happy!"

When you are again aware you will visualize your id/ego on the back of the gull. It spreads its wings and again you are aloft, flying back through the cloud, and again being bathed with all the colors of the spectrum, strengthening your id/ego to accept the imagery and the suggestions.

See yourself return; the gull steps on the blanket near your left shoulder. But this time it turns a brilliant white and disappears – to allow your id/ego to return in peace and harmony . . . peace and harmony. You will remain relaxed for a moment and then visualize the following imagery:

IMAGERY AND SUGGESTIONS:

You will create an image of yourself as the *person you want to be* (your success image). (You will learn how in Chapters 10 and 11.) Then you will give yourself these suggestions: "I am happy! I have self-confidence, self-assurance, and self-esteem!" Repeat this three times, then allow your eyes to open slowly – stretch – feel alert – smile and be happy!

Obviously you are not going to experience the full impact of the meditative procedure the first time you try, and obviously you are not going to get very far in training yourself to either procedure unless you practice conscientiously, mastering concentration first, then mastering meditation, then mastering meditative relaxation, and finally mastering astral projection.

Remember, you are learning procedures with which you probably have little experience and even less knowledge. Study the material on faith and belief – learn how to *let yourself go* – and you will, as so many already have, become adept in NovaYoga conditioning.

Alternate Bird Imagery

Most students of NovaYoga happily employ the seagull imagery and the beach scene as their relaxation image. However, there will be some where such imagery elicits little or no emotional involvement. If you have chosen a personal relaxation image (as described on page 96) then you can use another bird image in place of the seagull. For example, most persons react to a dove with pleasure. A dove has been employed in song and story as a symbol of peace and love, and as such will make a suitable alternate for the seagull.

Therefore, whatever your personal relaxation image may be, simply imagine a dove flying down and settling on your left shoulder . . . and the rest will be the same as the technique given on the previous pages.

Summary

Astral projection is more difficult to attain, as meditative relaxation was more difficult than simple meditation, and so on. Each step, however, conscientiously practiced, will condition your imaginative faculty. You are gaining more and more control and facility.

With astral projection you are brought full circle from simple hypnotic procedures to the most profound yoga meditation, wherein you can – and hopefully will – attain that state of altered consciousness, that serenity, that peace of mind that connotes total freedom from tension.

Chapter 9

How to Win Your Pearl of Great Price Through Mantra Meditation

MATTHEW (BOOK 13:46) speaks of a merchant who, when he found his pearl of great price, sold all his possessions (gave up everything) to possess it. Your pearl of great price (the reason you are applying yourself to Nova Yoga) is *to be the person you want to be.* To possess this, you too will give up that which now possesses you. You will give up your old habits, your old way of life, and of course your old (negative) self-image.

According to the suggested timetable given in Chapter 12, you will have reached this stage of your training in about six weeks. You are urged not to attempt any shortcuts – because there are none in the Pavlovian conditioning procedure. Empirically it has been determined that on the average it takes the conscientious student of NovaYoga about six weeks of practice to go through the series of training sessions starting with concentration and on through meditation, meditative relaxation, astral projection to mantra meditation. Many will take more time to reach this stage.

Granted that transcendental meditation and EEG instrument training both claim that they can train you in a matter of hours or days to reach that state of serenity that you are now preparing to reach with NovaYoga mantra meditation. The essential difference – restated – is that you have gone through an entire reconditioning, an entire mental housecleaning, to rid yourself of those inhibiting factors that have prevented you from attaining *self-realization* – that fulfillment that comes only with the knowledge that you are now at long last making full use of the innate talents, capabilities, and capacities that were your heritage.

You have a whole lifetime before you in which to enjoy your new Epicurean philosophy, your new self-confidence, your new self-assurance, your new self-esteem. And now you are going to crown your achievement with that training of your *imaginative faculty* that will bring you your assurance of total happiness – *tranquility*.

The NovaYoga Mantra Meditation Procedure

A mantra is, in Rajayoga, a mystical syllable, or a holy name for God, which is chanted constantly until one reaches a spell or mental state of ecstacy.

NovaYoga employs the mantra procedure, as it is the pathway to the deepest meditative state. However, the choice of the magical chant is not regarded with mysticism. On the contrary, there is a viable psychological modality that is employed for relaxation, which makes use of *sound* that is expressed with two syllables. A metronome, for example, emits a sound of two syllables. If you place one in front of you, adjusting the beat to approximately your pulse rate, concentrate on it, you will soon be in a state of utter relaxation.

The use of a mantra in yogic meditation, however, is for the purpose of limiting the intrusion of imagery –

without the tension of concentrated effort. The meditative state, as you have already been taught, is arrived at *not* by concentrating but rather by drifting in a state of passive reverie. The mantra in the background is an unobtrusive, yet important, aspect of your meditation. You quickly become accustomed to it and it becomes as natural to you as your breathing. It is then that it is most effective, because it keeps you in that middle state of consciousness – aware that you are aware and yet, in that hypnagogic state wherein you will emit alpha and/or theta rhymes, indicating total freedom from all tensions.

You may choose any two-syllable mantra you wish, but for the purpose of this training you will use the word *tranquil* – expressed as tran-quil, tran-quil, tran-quil. The choice, you will agree, is felicitious. The object of NovaYoga mantra meditation is to bring your awareness to the very center of your being, to your center of tranquility.

The procedure differs from previous training, in that you implant the imagery and suggestions *before* you enter the meditative state. You also set your mental clock for 15 minutes.

The Seeding Suggestions

The symbolism used here is taken from the real world. The Japanese pearl culturalist seeds his pearl oyster with a tiny piece of the pearlescent material taken from the shell of a particular oyster that is found in the mud flats of the Mississippi delta. His living oyster is then "planted," placed in a protected oyster bed where it is permitted to "mature."

Upon reaching maturity, the oyster is "unveiled" to reveal its "pearl of great price." So, too, do you seed your subconscious with the proper "pearlescence" (the image of the person you want to be). Your "pearl of great price" becomes your new personality, the person you want to be, when, following procedure, you are matured emotionally.

DO THIS:

1] You will meditate twice each day, in the morning and in the evening. You will rise from mantra meditation alert, bright, and eager, but completely tranquil. The same restrictions on pets, children, excessive noise, etc., apply. When you are ready, composed, close your eyes (lying down or sitting), say to yourself silently: "I am going into deep mantra meditation for 15 minutes, 15 minutes." Visualize the Yin/Yang briefly and let it dissolve into an image of yourself – as the person you want to be (you prod your imaginative faculty, if necessary, by talking to yourself, describing yourself as you want to be). When the image is set – that is, when you have fantasized sufficiently to establish the image clearly – you will say to yourself silently: "I am at peace . . . fully relaxed."

2] You will instantly visualize the "vaulted chamber" and the stream of liquid sunshine. Fix this image clearly with your mind's eye. See yourself floating in the vibrant stream and become aware of the brilliance of the Christ-light.

3] As you drift off in this vibrant stream, which will bring you to the center of your being – your center of tranquility – you begin your chant: "Tran-quil . . . tran-quil . . . tran-quil . . . tran-quil" (on and on). During all the time you are aware, don't try to concentrate, don't try to associate, just drift in passive reverie. You will have imagery at first which may be completely unrelated. It doesn't matter. Continue with your mantra as long as you are aware. Eventually, with much practice, you will lose your awareness and

pass into a state of oblivion, completely withdrawn from your reality. If you persist in your daily practice, eventually you should feel, when you reach oblivion – a state of ecstacy.

4] Your mental clock will bring you back to the awareness of your environment and you will say to yourself: "I am happy, I have self-confidence, self-assurance, and self-esteem." You will feel a keen sense of physical and mental well-being. Then slowly, gradually, stretch yourself, open your eyes, bright, alert, smiling, and happy!

Your Pearl of Great Price

Through constant practice you will soon become adept and will slip into deep mantra meditation – and oblivion. The "seeding suggestions," implanted before each session, are given the full benefit of your altered state of consciousness – because, freeing yourself of all tensions, you free your subconscious from all *negative self-imagery.* In its place now you are establishing your new, positive self-image of the person you want to be.

This new self-image is, of course, your "pearl of great price," and it becomes your primary motivational factor. Whereas until now your negative self-image had you self-conscious, self-defeating, self-abnegating – your dynamic, positive self-image will have you happy, self-confident, self-assured, and with that wonderful feeling of self-esteem which enables you – now – to actually *see* yourself as the person you want to be.

Summary

Mantra meditation is the final procedure you have to learn and practice in order to exercise that complete control of that wonderful power, your imaginative faculty.

Thomas Edison, an authentic American genius, had only three months' formal schooling. His early teachers thought him to be mentally defective. Yet this magnificent brain perfected well over 1,300 inventions for which he was issued patents. How did he do it?

In his laboratories at Menlo Park and West Orange, New Jersey there is his equipment, his effects, even his bed to which he retired every two or three hours. He told about it in his biography, claiming that every one of his inventions came from that bed!

There is no doubt that he was a "natural," a person with such inherent talent and capability that he soon found the one procedure that would enable him to extract (from his imaginative faculty) the ideas, improvements, and inventions that brought him fame and fortune. He found early that he could "think" best while relaxed, lying in bed, sleeping. However, it is evident from our present knowledge of the sleep state that he drifted into the meditative state . . . drifted in passive reverie . . . until he reached oblivion.

It is no longer possible, of course, but there can be little doubt that had he been checked by an electroencephalograph, he, while in his meditative state, would have been shown to be emitting theta rhythms as well as alpha. On "awakening" he would have his ideas, his solutions, his problems solved.

Chapter **10**

How to Overcome Your Negative Self-Image with Autosuggestion

Aristotle's maxim, "Nothing is in the mind that did not pass through the senses," we know, is literally true. You have already learned that it is your conscious mind, the area of your perceptions, that gives instructions, passes on suggestions, and so programs that subconscious computer of yours. This is accomplished by the use of imagery in your waking state of consciousness, as well as in the meditative state.

When you are relaxed in the meditative state, the critical faculty of your conscious mind is quiescent. The test of your depth of relaxation is a check of how completely quiescent your censor mechanism has become, because it is impossible to be physically relaxed and not be mentally relaxed (free of tension).

However, this critical faculty can relax and, in effect, become quiescent in the waking state with *repeated* suggestion. This is the basis for the Coué method of waking suggestion. It is because suggestions can slip by your critical faculty that it can be said, "autosuggestion is the uncritical acceptance of an idea."

We are all exposed to many forms of suggestions. We are assaulted daily with television and radio commercials which are actually dynamic forms of waking suggestions. They attempt to motivate us to "buy." In 1927 Claude C. Hopkins, dean of advertising men, said, "The power of all advertising lies in iteration and reiteration." He knew that if you were exposed to an advertising message only once or twice, you would not be affected. But when the message is repeated over and over, ad nauseam, you suspend your critical faculty by becoming barely conscious of the message. It is then that the message has its greatest effect, because then it becomes a subliminal suggestion.

Purely subliminal advertising was briefly tried on television some years ago. Pictures and taut messages were flashed on TV screens in mircosecond exposures, repeated over and over. These messages were of such short duration that the conscious mind could not perceive them. The cumulative effect of these repeated subliminal messages, however, created strong subconscious motivation. The Federal Communications Commission quickly banned the use of such subliminal advertising as an invasion of privacy.

We respond to suggestions throughout our lifetimes, starting as infants when we quickly accept the suggestion that mother's kiss will take away the sting of hurting from a cut finger.

We sometimes accept suggestions that are completely irrational, with no basis in fact, when mother tells us over and over again, "Harry is wonderful! Why can't you be like Harry?" Unfortunately, we accept the suggestion that Harry is indeed wonderful and that by comparison we are not, and thereby establish the basis for our subsequent feeling of inferiority.

The next time you are with a group, perhaps at a

party, try this experiment: Yawn – yawn widely so that you will be observed. Then observe the reaction. You will see, one after another, of your fellow partygoers yawning or stifling yawns. The power of suggestion.

Suggestion can lead a whole country to national suicide as in Hitler's Germany, or it can lead a whole country from a state of depression to prosperity as it did in the United States under the optimism of Roosevelt.

When bolstered with faith and belief, suggestion has led hundreds of pitifully maimed persons through the waters of the sacred grotto – healed miraculously.

The suggestions you will now learn to use in reconditioning yourself are autosuggestions; that is, they are suggestions you give yourself. These suggestions will reinforce the new positive self-images that are needed for your reconditioning. Perhaps the best-known exponent of autosuggestion was Emile Coué who lectured in this country in 1923. Coué made a point of impressing his audiences that *he* was not the healer, but rather that he taught others to *heal themselves*. He became well known in this country because of his lectures and his optimistic suggestion formula: "Every day in every way I am better and better!"

In this book, *Self-Mastery Through Conscious Auto Suggestion*, published in 1922 by the American Library Service, Coué wrote: "Autosuggestion is an instrument that we possess at birth, and which we play unconsciously all our life, but [it] is, however, a dangerous instrument because it can wound or even kill you. However, when you know how to employ it properly it can save your life!"

It is clear that Coué was referring to both negative and positive suggestions. You will now be taught how to formulate proper suggestions which will enable you to overcome your negative self-imagery. Establish the positive self-image of the person you want to be!

The Formulation of Suggestions

Do not give yourself more than one suggestion at a time. Thus if you are obese and smoke and wish to overcome both problems, start first with obesity. Ignore your smoking habit until you have slimmed yourself down, then start on your smoking problem.

Always give yourself suggestions in their simplest, most positive, form. Avoid negative implications. Do not say, "I will not be shy!" Say instead: "I am self-confident!" Do not say, "I will not be afraid of meeting people." Say instead: "I enjoy meeting people!" This principle is always the same whatever your problem may be. You will henceforth speak and think only in positive terms. If you find that you can't remember a name or a fact immediately, don't say, "I have a lousy memory!" but say, "I know the name; it will come to me in a moment!" Stop trying to recall; focus your mind on something else, and the name you're seeking will pop into your recollection without further scrunching of your forehead. Try it.

Do not be vague. Do not equivocate in formulating your suggestions. Do not expect your subconscious to interpret what it is you want to achieve. It is not going to reason out suggestions that are not properly spelled out. It can and will do exactly what you tell it to do if you express yourself in a positive form *and have the faith and belief that it will respond.*

Do not expect that your suggestions will become a conditioned reflex instantly. Remember the Pavlovian procedure of iteration and reiteration. (One young lady whose problem was obesity complained, "I still have a strong desire for chocolates even though I gave myself a suggestion that I would never eat another chocolate again in my life!") An impossible suggestion.

There is no magic. If you have practiced all the exercises diligently and conscientiously, with understanding and intelligence, the results can indeed be magical.

Keep in mind the Pavlovian principle of reconditioning. Any mind (he did it with dogs) can be conditioned, trained, taught, habituated, to accept suggestions if they are repeated simply, clearly, over and over again.

How long does such conditioning take? It differs with different persons. The factor that controls your ready acceptance of suggestions is your *critical faculty.* If you have trained yourself properly for total relaxation and can let yourself go, then your critical faculty is quiescent, not active, and hence does not analyze or otherwise obstruct the ready acceptance of your suggestions.

A second factor is motivation, which will be discussed in the next chapter. One young woman, with strong motivation, was able to condition herself to abandon her cigarette habit with only one session! Usually it takes five weeks.

Suggestions and Imagery

The effect of positive suggestion is magnified considerably when accompanied with *positive imagery.* As you have already learned from your practice of concentration, meditation, meditative relaxation, and mantra meditation, the image you form subconsciously is taken up by your imaginative faculty to become the dominant motivational force. When bolstered by your recognition of a series of small successes, it eventually becomes your new *positive self-image.* You have completely overcome your old, negative self-image!

Thus if you are shy because of deepseated feelings of inferiority (which is probably the most common hangup), you create a strong image of yourself in some situation that usually caused you most distress. See yourself being happy, confident, assured! With such an image, you will give yourself this suggestion: "I am happy! I enjoy meeting people!"

For total relaxation and peace of mind, go back to your practice with the Yin/Yang. Visualize it, go limp, give yourself the suggestion, "I am at peace . . . fully relaxed. . . ."

A fat person will picture himself thin. A smoker will picture himself discarding his cigarette habit down the toilet bowl. The student will picture himself reciting in class and gaining the approval of his instructor. Whatever your particular problem, picture yourself as having mastered it; see yourself now *enjoying* what you had previously dreaded doing.

The Basic Suggestions

The suggestions that have proved most effective empirically in a quarter of a century of practice are: "I am happy! I have self-confidence! I have self-assurance! I have self-esteem!" These are the ingredients of that assertive personality so desired by nearly everyone. When established as a conditioned reflex, they assure poise and a bearing of dignified composure which is the badge of the emotionally mature person.

In my practice as a teacher and counselor I have found that nearly everyone with whom I have had contact has a hangup that is evidenced by a particular behavioristic pattern. One is brash, loud, a poor listener because of compulsive self-interest. Another is shy, speaking in a hesitant, whispery voice, an equally poor listener who appears vague because of an equally compulsive self-interest. Between these two is the gamut of symptoms of inferiority, rejection, unworthiness – the underachievers. Add to these those with feelings of guilt who are either punishing themselves or others – it is not the wise child who knows its father but the fortunate child who recognizes its hangup and has the wisdom to do something about it.

Specialized Suggestions Employing More of Your Senses

In a study of memory and recall it was found that it is considerably more effective to establish an incident in your memory bank if you employ more of your senses in recognizing the incident initially. For example, the suggestions you wish to give to yourself may be lengthy, involved, and hence unwieldly in autosuggestion. But that can become effective if you engage more than just your imagination when you are in your relaxed state and ready for autosuggestion.

This is how you should proceed: before you go into relaxation, sit down at your table with paper and pencil and write your suggestion in complete detail. There is no need here to shorten it, because the entire suggestion will not be employed at the moment of your autosuggestion. You should now be familiar with the relaxed state of consciousness. You should know, therefore, that any mental exertion, concentration, or special effort at recall *could possibly negate your relaxation.* It is important that you give the autosuggestions in a manner that will not impose your critical faculty on it. In other words, your suggestions, accompanied by your positive self-imagery, should be accepted by your subconscious as any dream or reverie sequence is.

How, then, are you going to give yourself the lengthy, detailed suggestions you have just written out so painstakingly?

After you have written the suggestion, read it aloud. You are now engaging two, even three, senses; that is, the senses of sight, hearing, and touch (when writing out the suggestion). This means that many more of your brain's neurons were engaged in performing the task. Now that you have read it aloud, choose one or possibly two words that are the *key words,* that will always remind you of the complete suggestion. These key words are the only words you give yourself as autosuggestion. Now your subconscious will complete the recall of the total suggestion.

An excellent case in point is that of a middle-aged man who came to me for help. He had been employed as a chief clerk with a firm for 16 years. Now his firm was installing a computerized system and he had been told that he would be trained as a programmer. He had experienced panic. He was convinced that he was unable to handle this new task and was afraid he would have to quit his job altogether.

A fact which should have been evident to this man was pointed out to him: management does not choose a person for a particular job whom they feel is *unqualified.* On the contrary, the one best qualified, in their judgment, is chosen.

He reluctantly admitted the logic of this reasoning but still remained fearful. Then it was pointed out that his long tenure had proved his competency. No firm, no matter how badly managed, would continue in employment a person without competency at his job. He reluctantly admitted that, indeed, he was probably the one man in his firm who was best suited for this new work.

But he was still fearful. With all the assurances of logic given above, his lack of confidence in himself made him imagine failure and discharge – even after sixteen years! His was a classic example of an inferiority complex. But he was able to accept the idea that, once he had attained total release from tension, he would be able to overcome his fears (in fact, since his fears were the cause of his tension, he was able to accept the idea that he would become competent because he would be without fear).

He was told to visualize himself at his work in the computer room, free of all tension and worry, completely competent, therefore self-confident and self-assured; moreover, he was *proud.* (Thus he could develop his self-esteem.) He was hesitant, at first, but did accept the suggestion that he create such an image in fantasy.

When the suggestions were discussed, he felt that the basic suggestions were insufficient. He needed more than generalities. Therefore he was instructed to write, in complete detail, the suggestions he *knew* would give him the self-confidence he was seeking. They were: "I am the programmer! I am envied by all my associates because it was I who was chosen above them all for this job! I am fully competent! I know the work perfectly! My boss is happy with me! He is going to give me a raise! I am envied by everyone!"

This is an example of the kind of suggestion you should *not* try to give yourself as autosuggestion. If your problem requires this kind of suggestion and you know that a lengthy, detailed suggestion would work for you, then do as he did – write it in complete detail and select any *two* words as the key words that will represent the entire suggestion.

The two words this man chose were *envy* and *raise.* He was trained to proceed with his exercises and give himself these words in autosuggestion: "I am happy! Envy . . . raise . . . envy . . . raise . . . envy . . . raise . . . !" He would repeat the words over and over until he slipped off into normal, physiological sleep.

The secret of the success of such prerelaxation suggestion is based on Coué's conscious suggestion procedure. Actually, your subconscious mind is being programmed, with complete approval of your critical faculty, in the waking state. And it is being made more effective by employing more of your senses. Therefore when the key words are given, the entire suggestion is recalled by your subconscious without altering your state of relaxation – remaining quiescent and relaxed.

Suggestions Condition and Recondition

Your present personality pattern is the result of your early-conditioning life experiences. Whatever negative self-imagery you now possess resulted from the negative suggestions that slipped past your critical faculty and were accepted by your subconscious – as a negative self-image.

Your problem now is to overcome the effects of your negative self-image. It is a matter of reconditioning. You erase a negative image by overcoming it with a positive self-image! Since this principle was discovered by Pavlov in 1904, it has been proved by thousands of successful instances of reconditioning.

Your faith and belief and your eventual conviction are all related reconditioning experiences. As you study and apply yourself to the exercises of NovaYoga, you will inevitably become aware of your small successes, and these will become the mortar that will cement the structure of your new personality pattern and your final conviction, which signals your successful reconditioning! You will have become the person you want to be.

The Quiescent Critical Faculty

The only factor that can work against your subconscious acceptance of autosuggestion is your critical faculty. If, for example, you weigh 269 pounds and you want to reduce to your proper weight of 175 pounds, your autosuggestion would be: "I am happy! I am losing five pounds every week! I am 175 pounds!"

These suggestions are from an actual case. A young man was instructed using these suggestions and apparently accepted them but reported a week later that he hadn't lost a pound. When questioned, he explained that when he gave himself these suggestions he mentally rejected them as being silly! "I'm not 175 pounds! I'm a fat 269, and I can't kid myself!"

He had a problem. His critical faculty was obviously not quiescent; he should have been able to drift off into reverie during meditative relaxation. He had not understood the basic procedure. He didn't realize that it was necessary that he suspend normal reason and logic and release his imaginative faculty to create the image of himself as being 175 pounds.

It was necessary for him to go back and spend more time practicing concentration and meditation before attempting meditative relaxation. Then perhaps he would be able to fantasize and let himself go in a state of reverie.

Remember: the procedure is dynamic. It requires not only your understanding but your acquiescence in the creative process of controlled reverie.

Practice each exercise until you can truly let yourself go.

Summary

Suggestion is the process of implanting imagery, information, or a response from some stimulus within the memory bank. According to Isaac Asimov you have the capacity of storing a million-billion "bits" of such information.

These suggestions are received and stored most

effectively when they are accepted uncritically, for "autosuggestion is the uncritical acceptance of an idea."

All suggestions are the basis of your conditioning. In other words, your conditioned responses to circumstances within your environment add up to your personality pattern. Some of these conditioned responses add up also to what may be called your hangups.

It is for the purpose of overcoming these negative conditioned responses that you are studying NovaYoga – to be the person you want to be.

Chapter 11

How to Use the Power of Proper Motivation

MOTIVATION IS THAT something which prompts a person to act in a certain way or that determines volition. It can be either conscious or subconscious.

An example of a conscious motivation is when a football team rated by the experts as the underdog goes out on the playing field *motivated* to win because their coach (Knute Rockne was famous for his ability to motivate his teams) gave them such a pep talk that their will to win gave them that extra something that enabled them to win.

However, it is the subconscious motivations that are the subject of our inquiry. Why, for example, would a pretty girl allow herself to become fat and ugly? One answer to this is that she eats too much of the wrong foods, to satisfy some subconscious motivation perhaps. Her eating habit has become a compulsion.

Her subconscious motivation is powerful. Despite the evidence of her eyes, she continues to eat and eat. Such a girl often has a subconscious craving for love (which as a child she felt was denied her) and food, especially candy and other sweets, becomes a symbol of love. Her overeating becomes a conditioned reflex; much the same as the smoker who unconsciously reaches for a cigarette when nervous or uneasy, she reaches for a chocolate or a sweet when subconsciously she feels herself unloved.

Motivation of this type is a powerful force and is often used to attain some goal to assure ego-satisfaction. Witness the small man who develops an aggressive manner because subconsciously he craves the ego-satisfaction of demonstrating his equality, or better, his superiority to the tall person. (This is so common a characteristic that psychologists refer to it as the Napoleonic complex.)

You yourself have to be properly motivated in order to overcome a personality problem or hangup or simply to improve yourself. Otherwise, your application to NovaYoga will not produce the wonderful results you hope to attain. I hope to be able to help you find and develop your most powerful motivation by showing you how it is done.

First we must understand that many persons actually do not wish to overcome their negative personality self-images. Whatever their overt symptom – excessive smoking, excessive eating, excessive drinking, excessive shyness, excessive self-conciousness, excessive aggressiveness, excessive mannerism of all sorts are symptoms of subconscious motivations which are maintained because they satisfy a subconscious compulsion.

It isn't enough for you to say "Yeah! But in my case I really want to change!" Every one of the symptoms mentioned above is the reason why these persons came to NovaYoga for help. Every one stoutly maintained, "Yeah! I really want to change!" And not one really wanted to change! Consciously they knew they had to do something, but subconsciously they negated every effort to overcome their problems – until they were able to face the causal factors, their early experiences, through introspection. (You learned how to do this in meditation.)

It is possible that you may not have to probe deeply into your childhood to find the reasons why you are now what you are. You may be prepared to accept all the suggestions – all the new positive self-imagery, all the small successes, and speedily reach that state of total conviction when you will be the person you want to be.

Later in this book I will detail the experiences of two men who wanted to quit smoking. One required long and painstaking training, with introspection which revealed sufficient reasons that could be rationalized at an adult level. The other, however, had powerful conscious motivation. He had been told by his doctor that he had a spot on his lungs. The only possible chance he had to stay alive was to quit smoking. He tried on his own but failed and finally in desperation came to NovaYoga. He required only one session in meditative relaxation to set his new self-image, and he never smoked another cigarette.

In the next chapter you will be given a step-by-step procedure of how to apply the lessons you have learned from previous chapters. You will be given two approaches. One is the behavioristic procedure, which employs four tapes (which you can obtain from me or make for yourself). This procedure is based on your being sufficiently (consciously) motivated to require little or no introspection. The second approach is the introspection procedure, which requires sufficient introspective probing to develop powerful subconscious motivation. This is what I am reviewing for you now.

You must go back to Chapter 2 and review "How You Developed Your Present Personality." This chapter gives you the psychological explanations of how and why you developed feelings of inferiority. An excellent case in point was a young man who came to NovaYoga for help. He was 28 and had never slept with a girl. He desperately wanted to develop the courage to approach a girl he admired. Introspection revealed that in his early childhood his mother, who was good and loving, became annoyed with him as a child because he was forever under her feet. She used to say to him, "Why can't you be like Harry? Harry is wonderful! Everybody likes Harry! Harry . . . Harry. . . !"

Although he had been conscious that he had always disliked Harry, he had never thought to find out why. He thought only that he disliked him because of Harry's ability with girls. The more he thought about Harry and his girls, the more he felt himself retreating into himself. However, he speedily went back into his childhood when he learned meditative relaxation and remembered his early resentment against his mother! He felt a guilt for having hated his mother! But the real, underlying reason for his present feelings of inferiority was his conditioned response to his mother's constant whining.

When he recognized this he was able to rationalize, because he had actually developed skills that made him superior to Harry, and he readily accepted the image of himself having girls. Now that he could feel himself equal to (or even superior to) Harry, he could also visualize himself equal to Harry's way with girls!

He was therefore powerfully motivated by his new subconscious image of himself – winning away Harry's girls!

Now it is necessary to give you an example, a woman who subconsciously did not wish to change her personality symptom. She came to NovaYoga with a decided stutter and after sufficient training in meditative relaxation was able to go into introspection and recall the incidents, as a child, when she not stutter (in fact, when her teacher called her the best reader in the class!). She was then able to recall when she began to stutter.

Her stutter began when she was accused by her mother of going through her mother's bureau drawers. She was punished for this by her mother saying: "Wait till your father comes home! He'll give it to you!" She actually looked forward to this because her father, whom she adored, was undemonstrative, and she longed to have him hug her!

But when her father came home he was tired and irritable. Instead of spanking her as they both wished (she and her mother) he merely told her to go to bed without any supper! She did and cried herself to sleep. She felt total rejection from both parents. So the next day, when she told her next-door friend, a girl two years older, she was pleased when her friend sympathized with her. She had found a mother-surrogate.

The reason she now resisted stopping her stuttering was that she was now living with another girl, another in a long line of mother-surrogates! She had become homosexual.

"As a Man Thinketh in His Heart, So Is He"

You are motivated, whether consciously or subconsciously, by whatever images you maintain within your imaginative faculty. If you are content with yourself as you are now then obviously you are motivated to retain your *status quo*. But if you aren't completely satisfied and wish to improve it, then you have apparently recognized that you do possess innate talents and capabilities which you have not realized and that, therefore, you are underachieving.

This is your first requirement. You will find it fairly easy to accept this evaluation of yourself. But it is amazing how many people cannot take that first step. They feel their lack of fulfillment is not due to any failure on their part but simply to circumstances, luck, fate, whatever, but certainly it isn't their doing.

Perhaps the first fact to consider and accept is that

accepting the idea that you are an underachiever does not castigate you or place any blame on you. On the contrary, recognizing that you do have talents and capabilities which you haven't been able to use properly merely indicates that there are some obstacles between you and your self-realization. Simply put, you are going to recognize these obstacles and remove them!

What I have been saying to you about motivation can now be expressed as removing the obstacles that are preventing you from making full use of your innate talents and capabilities. The moment these obstacles are removed (the moment you change your negative self-image) you will have such powerful motivation to self-fulfillment that you will soon become the person you want to be!

A young man on the New York police force – six feet tall, weighing 200 pounds – had a problem related to his masculinity. He could respond to the several meditative procedures. He attained sufficient relaxation but could not respond to autosuggestion, which had him powerful, sexually and physically.

He had to be *motivated.* It was important that he develop that subconscious motivation which would establish the strong, masculine image as the drive that would give impetus to his conscious expression and overcome his conscious evaluation of himself as being inadequate sexually.

He resisted but eventually was able to recall early incidents that were traumatic. He first remembered himself as a small child of six, fat and lonely, seeking the companionship of boys in his neighborhood, all of whom were older and bigger than he. The leader of the group unfortunately was a bully who decided to have some fun with this little boy of six. He organized an "initiation." The boy was to lower his pants and be spanked. But when he did lower his pants, everyone laughed as the bully jeeringly pointed to the size of the little boy's penis. True, it was small.

The boy couldn't stand the laughter. He picked up his pants and ran home, crying. After that the same boys made him the butt of their jokes, always teasing him about his penis. From this early experience the man had come to think of himself as being inadequate.

He had to create a new image that would motivate him positively. The fact that he was now a policeman helped, because, although he had long since lost contact with these boys, he did learn that the instigator of the "initiation," the bully, was now a gangster and in prison. It didn't take him very long to visualize himself as being superior to this bully. In fact, he allowed himself to fantasize his early experience. He saw himself in the same situation, but instead of running away he stood up to the bully, because he saw himself as a policeman who arrested the bully and put him in jail.

He accepted the image of himself as being superior, because in adult life he had achieved the status of a policeman. Seeing himself strong and powerful, instead of the fat, lonely little child, enabled him to accept the suggestion that he was now strong and powerful. The image became the motivating force that enabled him to overcome his hangup.

There is probably no one, born to wealth or poverty, who has not some personality characteristic, some hangup, which prevents him from attaining personal self-fulfillment.

Summary

Your strongest motivation to attain self-realization is to find and overcome that early incident that was the cause of your present hangups. Once you recognize it (or them, since there may be more than one), you will use your imaginative faculty, combined with rationalism. In the case of the policeman, it wasn't difficult for him to imagine himself as being a policeman as a small child. A policeman's image is one of masculinity, strength. This enabled him to accept an image of himself as being superior to his early tormentor – and hence more masculine.

Or, as in the case of the man who disliked his older brother Harry. He found it easy to accept the image of himself as being superior because he actually had developed superior skills.

Or, as in the case of the clerk who was being trained as a computer programmer. He was able to accept the image of himself as a successful programmer because of the status this new job gave him. Remember his suggestions? Raise and envy! He wanted the others to envy him! Because of this, he was powerfully motivated.

Follow the same procedure – find your own conscious or subconscious motivation and use it to become the person you want to be.

William James, the great American psychologist and author of *The Principles of Psychology,* had this to say about motivation: "If you wish to be rich, you will be rich; if you wish to be good, you will be good. Only you must then really wish these things, and wish them with exclusiveness, and not wish, at the same time, a hundred other incompatible things just as strongly!"

Chapter 12

How to Be the Person You Want to Be

ALL NEW STUDENTS of NovaYoga are required to read this book twice – first, as though it were a novel, to get the feeling, and second to begin the exercises. Take Chapters 3 and 4 together. They will start you off nicely, because you may be assured of a keener sense of physical well-being in a surprisingly short time, especially if you haven't been exercising before. This is all you should do for the first two weeks. It is expected that you will develop a rhythm of habituation that will become a part of your new life style.

In two weeks you will be ready to tackle *concentration*. Chapter 5 is extremely important, especially if you are a student. It may very probably be the first mental discipline to which you submit yourself. For that reason it should not be lightly skimmed.

Everyone's mind skips from image to image, like a grasshopper, whenever they are trying to focus their mind on something they have little interest in or something (or subject) in which they feel themselves inferior or inadequate. When you are afraid of something subconsciously because you feel you are not capable enough or smart enough to succeed at it, your mind will skip about.

Such negative feelings are nonsense, but telling you so isn't going to help you or convince you. If you are a genuine underachiever and you consistently belittle yourself and your capabilities, you are going to have to really struggle with that grasshopper mind of yours by applying yourself seriously to the practice of NovaYoga.

Since you have read (and so, in effect, listened to me) and hopefully understood the various facets of NovaYoga training, we must have established some rapport. By now you should be able to accept what I say to you without that oh-yeah attitude. So I expect that you will accept my assurance that you will be able to train yourself to concentrate on any subject, whether you like it or dislike it, *if* you will follow the instructions and practice.

Practice is the key! There's no magic about it, except if you consider Pavlov's reconditioning magical. Because that's what you will be doing – conditioning yourself to control your imaginative faculty.

The mental exercise of concentration is actually no different from the physical exercises of muscular repose. The results are the same. In both, you strengthen muscles. And whereas you don't think of your brain as having muscles, it does have brain cells, neurons, which you are programming. What you will be doing is to make real what can be regarded as a minor miracle.

Your imaginative faculty is that unique human capability that enables you to use that fabulous computer memory bank of yours in the creation (or in simple recall) of bits of information that are stored in your brain. It has been calculated that your brain has a storage capacity of one quadrillion bits of information – that's a million times a billion. Try belittling yourself now.

Neuroanatomists, psychologists, molecular biologists, and biochemists are now in general agreement that you have two types of memory. Short-term memory may last only a few moments (recalling a telephone number long enough to dial). Long-term memory is stored for life. Dr. Wilder Penfield, the Canadian brain surgeon, touched various points in patient's brains with a low-voltage probe. One woman heard Christmas carols in a church she attended as a child; another relived the birth of her child 20 years before.

Theoretically you should be able to push a mental key (or meditate with free association) and get computerized information retrieval of any life experience from the moment of your birth. The main reason you can't is the same reason why you think you are inadequate or inferior. You *inhibit* your creativity; you stifle your imaginative faculty; you accept the unrewarding role of an underachiever because you allow mental blocks to interfere with the efficient working of that magnificent computer of yours. These mental blocks are the hangups you are trying to overcome by studying NovaYoga.

I don't know how long it will take you to master concentration. Some do it in a week, others take longer, but only when you feel that you have acquired satisfactory facility in controlling grasshopper imagery should you go on to the study and practice of meditation. This, as explained, is an extension of concentration, but with the focus on learning how to control free-association imagery.

Association is the process of relating an object or an individual to a particular image, which aids retrieval. Dr. Fergus Craik of the University of Toronto explained the reason you didn't instantly recognize that man who smiled at you when you were crossing the street is that your association with that particular face is at the supermarket checkout counter. (You've never seen him anywhere else.) All memory-training courses teach similar association procedures to help you with your recall.

However, the aspect of association in which we are

primarily interested is emotional. This is what Freud explored in his search for causal factors. His procedure of free association is to help you dredge up apparently long-forgotten incidents which have an emotional association with the imagery on which you are meditating.

As with your practice of concentration, it is suggested that you continue with meditation, following the instructions and the examples, until you are able to recall incidents in your childhood which may be causal factors. This is the process of introspection.

DO THIS:

Now that you are well along with your visceral exercises – your breathing, have practiced concentration satisfactorily and having performed introspection via the meditative procedure – you are ready to complete your "personality inventory questionnaire."

The purpose of the questionnaire is to enable you to express yourself and, in effect, to verbalize your problem much the same as you would in my office. By reviewing yourself objectively, in terms of your personality problem, you will be able to crystallize your symptoms and be able to understand how they relate to causal factors.

Very often, merely by the act of writing the answers to such questions it has been possible to reevaluate oneself and his thinking and better understand how one is to readjust and recondition himself to become the person he wants to be.

You may prefer to copy the questions and list your answers on a separate sheet of paper. The answers must be revealing, totally frank, totally objective. You will not equivocate and certainly will not alter obvious facts.

After you have completed the questionnaire you should understand yourself a little better – appreciate your innate talents, capabilities, and capacities, be able to establish your success image as goal – the objective you hope to attain as a result of your study and application to NovaYoga.

Personality Inventory Questionnaire

1. State your problem; give details: . . . .
2. How long have you had the problem? . . . .
3. What do the symptoms keep you from doing? . . . . . .
4. What conditions affect these symptoms? . . . .
5. What will you do when you overcome the symptoms? . . . .
6. What is your attitude toward the opposite sex? . . . . .
7. Was your childhood happy or unhappy? . . . .
8. What sort of person was your father to you as a child? . . . .
9. What sort of a person was your mother to you as a child? . . . .
10. What was the relationship between your mother and father when you were a child? Did they argue, and did you see them argue? . . . .
11. Where were you in terms of your brothers and sisters? . . . .
12. What were your feelings about your nearest brother or sister? . . . .
13. Were you happy in school? . . . . . . If unhappy, why? . . . .
14. Give details of traumatic incidents, experiences that made you painfully unhappy (deaths, accidents, illnesses, embarrassing moments, sex) . . . . . .
15. Do you lack self-confidence . . . . . . Always? . . . . . . Sometimes? . . . . . . State areas wherein you exhibit most lack of self-confidence: . . . .
16. Are you able to admit your mistakes? . . . .

17. Do you believe yourself right and think others are to blame?............................

18. Are you interested only in yourself, indifferent to others? ....

19. Are you uncomfortable around others, usually avoid them?............................

20. Are you generally pessimistic, expect the worst to happen?............................

21. Do you feel guilt about something?............. What? ....

22. Are you sensitive about criticism?..............

23. Do you feel everyone is picking on you?......Your mother?......Your father?......Teacher?...... School acquaintances?......Friends?...........

24. Do you put things off?......Then forget about them? ....

25. Do you lack self-assurance?......................

26. Do you have self-esteem?.........................

27. Do you form rigid opinions and resent change?....

28. Do you dislike your present life?................

29. Do you always feel you are getting a raw deal?.....

30. Do you like your mother?......Father?...... Brother(s)?......Sister(s)? ....

By now you should have a fair idea of negative and positive personality patterns. State what you think is your negative self-image: ....

....

State what you think is your positive self-image:.........

....

State and give details of your earliest recollection at the conscious level:...........................

....

State what you believe to be your need for rationalization (in terms of your likes and dislikes) (see number 30 above): ....

....

As you progress with your study and application of NovaYoga, you will begin to observe small successes. Begin to list them here:............................

....

State when you have reached conviction:............

EXPLANATION

Questions *1* to *14* are to help you understand yourself objectively and to aid you, not only during your introspection, but in the framing of your suggestions. Questions *15* to *29* relate to your personality pattern. If you can recognize yourself in these questions as being negative – an under-achiever lacking in self-confidence, self-assurance, and self-esteem – then you will probably "see" yourself in one or more of the case histories given in Part Two. You should study these case histories and note the procedures followed. Question 30 and the statements: causal factors are generally found in your relationship with your mother and/or father and/or the authority figure who dominated your early life. When, during introspection, such causal factors are recalled, rationalization is to be used to wash out its effect. Finally, your new positive image is to be superimposed in order to establish a new, positive subconscious motivation.

NOW DO THIS:

1] (*Chapter 7*): Begin the study of meditative relaxation, which is the yogic form of hypnosis, by memorizing the procedure. Select a time and place when you will be undisturbed by pets, children, telephones, or noise.

You will learn this as a *ritual*, a sort of prayer or chant, developing a rhythm between your silent . . . mental . . . verbalization and your physical relaxation response. The object of this training is to prepare you for a *state of altered consciousness* during which you will experience the alpha and/or theta rhythms. It is when you have trained yourself to slip readily into the *hypnagogic sleep state* that the critical faculty of your conscious mind will become *quiescent*.

Meditative relaxation is a somewhat strange state of consciousness which requires some explanation (although you should be completely familiar with it, since you experience it naturally every day). It is a state of consciousness that is neither sleep nor waking. It is a state of consciousness wherein you are *passively*, rather than critically, aware, as in the waking state. With practice you will lose your awareness of your immediate environment, although you will not lapse into the delta, or unconscious, level. This is known as deep trance. Think of it as a method of controlled daydreaming in which your consciousness allows you to be part of the dream without exercising any mental *effort* or *concentration* – you merely accept your awareness passively as you become more and more relaxed, physically and mentally.

It is while you are in this altered state of consciousness that you accept your new success image and your autosuggestions – without critical resistance. For example, if you weigh 230 pounds and want to weigh 175, you create an image of yourself as 175 pounds and say to yourself silently: "I am a hundred and seventy-five pounds."

If you haven't reached the deep-trance state described

above, your critical faculty should still be alert and you should reject the image and the suggestion (you *know* you are a fat 230 pounds).

Therefore, when you have trained yourself to reach the deep-trance state, you will be employing a biofeedback procedure. Your metabolic function will begin to adjust to this new subconscious self-image, and, assuming you follow the diet suggested, you will find yourself losing weight.

This same procedure – allowing the conscious mind to relax and become quiescent and then creating an image of blood flowing from your brain to your hands, saying: "My hands are hot because the blood is flowing into them from my brain . . . my hands are hot . . ." – has been used successfully in biofeedback training to overcome migraine headaches.

You will continue with your practice of meditative relaxation until you have reached satisfactory relaxation. On the average, it takes about two weeks of practice to attain a satisfactory conditioned reflex.

The procedure will follow the detailed instructions given in Chapter 7, followed by the autosuggestions: "I am happy, I have self-confidence, self-assurance and self-esteem" – repeated three times, followed by drifting off into a normal, natural physiological sleep.

2] (*Chapter 8*): Your next step is to train yourself in astral projection. In classic yoga this is given only in very advanced studies, and the objective is quite different. In NovaYoga, astral projection is used to furnish your imaginative faculty with imagery that will enable you to release your id/ego from the control of your critical faculty. Thus you are able to enter the deepest state of altered consciousness in preparation of your reach for your center of tranquility.

Symbolism, as part of this technique, becomes important, because as it is understood and accepted by your conscious mind it becomes a powerful subconscious force for psychosomatic response.

It usually takes only about a week to establish the imagery. You can practice astral projection while you are performing meditative relaxation. Remember, the latter is performed only when you are ready for sleep – drifting off into deep, natural sleep at the conclusion of the suggestions.

Astral projection can be performed at odd times other than in bed just before sleep – perhaps in the morning just after you've done the exercises or in the evening after dinner. Fifteen minutes only!

The result should be to bring you into a very deep, relaxed state of consciousness. Remember, the entire procedure employs specific symbols which, when understood, have a profound psychosomatic effect, particularly when this procedure is merged into mantra meditation, which you will learn to perform in Chapter 9.

3] (*Chapter 9*): NovaYoga mantra meditation is the final and ultimate meditative state. It closely follows the classic form. It has as its objective the attainment of *oneness with the Absolute,* which is a profound and unique altered state of consciousness. It is possible with long and patient practice not only to achieve a state of tranquility (a state of consciousness wherein you rise above the limitations of your physical as well as psychic environments) but to experience that rare state of exaltation that has been described by the eminent scholar, Dr. Richard Buche, as cosmic consciousness. This is a state of ineffable delight, beyond description. Perhaps one word may approach it – *ecstasy* – such physical, mental, and spiritual bliss that can be considered as being "otherworldly," out of this world, certainly out of the reach of any experience you may consider normal. But don't expect to reach this state without much practice.

Mantra meditation, as you will first approach it and as you will practice and train yourself to perfect, has a practical objective. It is that objective toward which you set yourself when you began your study of NovaYoga: to overcome your hangups and thereby become the person you want to be.

In the Bible (Matthew 13:46) we read the story of the merchant who, when he found a pearl of great price, sold all that he owned to possess it. By analogy you are that merchant and you are seeking *your* pearl of great price, your new personality, your freedom from tensions, your freedom from hangups – the person you want to be. You must be prepared to give up everything, including your present life pattern, and build for yourself a new and enlightened life style because of your *release* from the emotional shackles that have bound you and have prevented you from developing the God-given talents, capabilities and capacities with which you were born.

I know that you will say: "I will give up these – gladly!" Still, it is the insidious nature of such conditioning that although you consciously desire to give up old and bad habits, subconsciously their roots will resist change so powerfully that many will give up the struggle and retain their old, inhibiting life style.

It is possible that "giving up your present life style" may mean an actual *change in your social environment* (such a change was needed by the woman described in Chapter 16). This is not advocated as a general rule. But, you can understand why such a move may be essential. Circumstances, or individuals, over which, or whom, you have no control, may effectively block your efforts at constructive change. In such instances it may be necessary for you to consider a complete alteration in your physical and/or social environment.

Your Small Successes Lead to Conviction

When you have reached this stage of your study and practice of NovaYoga, you must become alert to your *small successes*. As you practice, as you meditate, as you continue to give yourself suggestions to bolster your new success image, you will soon find yourself doing and acting as you have always wanted but never have been able to do or act before. This simply means that you are experiencing biofeedback. Your new image is motivating you. An example of such a small success is described in Chapter 13, in which I tell you how I developed and employed NovaYoga to overcome a truly distressing personality problem.

It is when you begin to enjoy what you had formerly dreaded doing, when you find yourself leading a group instead of merely following as usual, when you observe yourself now as being tranquil whereas before you were worried and tense, when you begin to recognize that you are *unconsciously* enjoying every moment of your reality – then you are indeed experiencing your series of small successes, which will lead you to conviction. When this happens, you have overcome your problem forever.

The End Is only the Beginning

You are now ready to begin your study and practice of NovaYoga. Chapter 12 is really Chapter 1, in that it is the guide to your study and practice.

Part Two of this book is a series of case histories. I call it "NovaYoga in Action." I could relate a great many more success stories, but these are the most typical and serve to demonstrate the procedure. I hope, too, that you will be tolerant and bear with me long enough to allow me to tell you how and when I first became interested in yoga and self-image psychology. (I relate this in Chapter 13.)

Finally, after more than a quarter of a century of a varied but mostly successful empirical practice counseling the underachiever, I am convinced that real and lasting success in developing emotional maturity is best attained by means of an autogenous procedure.

The various schools from which I have borrowed – Freud to Watson with James and Pavlov in between, as well as the several schools of yoga – have all contributed to the structuring of NovaYoga autogenic procedure, offering, I believe, better supportive help than group therapies. For despite the lamentations of the poet, man *is* an island unto himself, and only he alone can experience that joy, that ecstasy, that bliss of tranquility that is within his reach because of the Godlike faculty he alone possesses – his imagination!

The Inevitable Comparisons

It is inevitable that some kind of controversy will develop between the proponents of EEG instrument training (to experience alpha); Transcendental meditation (to reach a state of emotional serenity); and NovaYoga.

There really is no basis for any such controversy. Each method has its merits; its successes and its failures. However, let us examine each procedure to determine whether there is any basis for controversy.

What is the goal of each procedure?

The goal of *instrument training* (using an electroencephalograph or the simpler, portable electroencephalophone) is to develop the ability to reach a state of altered consciousness that is characterized by alpha brain waves.

Dr. Joe Kamiya, and many sleep psychologists who have substantiated Dr. Kamiya's research, has demonstrated that the alpha rhythm [with occasional bursts of theta rhythms] is characteristic of the meditative state of yoga meditators and Zen meditators. When the subject is emitting alpha and/or theta rhythms he experiences a sense of euphoria.

The goal of Transcendental meditation is essentially the same as the goal for instrument training, obviously, because EEG training appeared to be a "short-cut" to the meditative state. However, the very long period of training and practice normally associated with the classic yoga or Zen schools has been overcome, apparently, by the teaching of the Maharishi Mahesh Yogi. Whereas it takes the average student of yoga two years (and the Zen student even longer) to attain that state of serenity which characterizes the successful meditative state of consciousness, the transcendental method is learned after only four lessons. Individual success, of course, is extremely variable and depends on the amount of practice. The concensus, insofar as it has been ascertained, is that it averages from six months to a year for the real benefits to accrue.

The goal of NovaYoga is self-realization . . . with such self-realization understood as the ability to experience self-fulfillment that comes with recognizing and exploiting one's innate talents, capabilities and capacities. This, frequently, involves a positive self-image alteration in one's personality pattern – to become the person you want to be!

The greatest difficulty with all three procedures is to learn how to let yourself go! Whereas there is no specific instruction or training in this phase of the practice of either EEG or TM procedures – there is a definite program of training to attain this facility when practicing NovaYoga. It begins with the recognition that yoga is the oldest form of hypnotic/meditative training (this is probably the one point of controversy because the classic yoga proponent will deny this).

There are four training stages leading to the final tranquility of mantra meditation. These are:

1] SELF-HYPNOSIS – a yogic form of imagination-manipulation which trains you to the fundamentals of mental and physical relaxation to experience alpha and freedom of all tension;

2] ASTRAL PROJECTION – wherein you learn to place your conscious mind into quiescence by projection of your id/ego to your inner space and the portal of your center of tranquility;

3] PAVLOVIAN RECONDITIONING – which employs your training to "let yourself go" and establishes your new, positive self-image of the person you want to be . . . which thereafter acts as your primary motivational force;

4] NOVAYOGA MANTRA MEDITATION – which now takes all this training to seed your subconscious with your new self-imagery, allowing it to germinate and to mature as your pearl of great price – that new personality of the person you want to be; mature, tranquil.

The only comparison that can be made between these three procedures, therefore, is that they each touch in the area of one's experience with the alpha and/or theta brain rhythms. If this is all that you wish to attain then either EEG or TM will satisfy you. They are, both, viable procedures and recommended. However, if you have a hangup; a personality problem; if you are uptight and find it virtually impossible to let yourself go, then NovaYoga training is indicated . . . to help you, guide you to become the person you want to be!

A Word about Cassette Tapes

To overcome your hangups, achieve tranquility, and become the person you want to be, you will require nothing more than conscientious application, study, and practice of the physical and mental exercises detailed in *The NovaYoga Technique of Self-Realization.* This is the book that every one of my subjects is required to read, study, and apply.

However, private sessions are costly and to aid in speedier reconditioning I employ an exclusive recording technique. Because cassette recorders are now inexpensive (and most subjects are already equipped), I produce a series of four tapes which are sufficient in reconditioning the average problem. These are as follows:

1] MEDITATIVE RELAXATION – to quickly train you to overcome physical and mental tension, to experience the alpha rhythm.

2] ASTRAL PROJECTION – to train you to experience deeper states of altered consciousness and bring you to your center of tranquility.

3] PAVLOVIAN RECONDITIONING – to recondition your negative self-image and to establish your new, positive success image.

4] NOVAYOGA MANTRA MEDITITION – to train you to the deepest yoga meditation; to experience samadhi; to attain your pearl of great price; peace; tranquility; manifest your new self as the person you want to be.

Tapes *1* and 3 are listened to by using a private earphone, at night, in bed, as you drift off to sleep. Tape 1 for two weeks, Tape 3 for as long as you feel it necessary (when you actually begin to feel and act as your new success image suggests).

Tapes 2 and *4* are wake-up tapes; that is, they are listened to twice each day, morning and evening (not in bed). Tape 2 for two weeks, Tape 4 as long as necessary until you are able to wean yourself away from dependency on my voice – performing entirely on your own.

I repeat: such tapes are employed to *speed* reconditioning. However, the NovaYoga technique of self-realization is an autogenic procedure; that is, it is self-produced or self-generated. Simply by investing the time in applying yourself to the procedure until you acquire the proper facility, this book alone will help you, guide you, recondition you, to become the person you want to be.

PART TWO

NovaYoga in Action

CASE HISTORIES

A NOTE ON THE CASE HISTORIES:
The references quoted describing the experiences of students of NovaYoga have been altered to avoid direct quotation to prevent recognition of the individuals themselves. The facts are, nonetheless, true and are used to illustrate a point or principle in the text.

Chapter 13

How I Overcame My Own Stutter

I WAS TRYING to get a liberal arts education in 1923 as a background for my English major. I hoped to become a writer. Somerset Maugham had become a successful writer despite a bad stutter and I thought that perhaps I could too.

My depression was compounded by poverty. I was the youngest of a large family, and when I came along my brothers and sisters were nearly grown; before I reached college age they had all left. My father's earnings alone weren't enough to maintain the home and me in what he considered was idleness.

We lived in a coldwater railroad flat on East 77th Street in Manhattan, near Avenue A, which is now York Avenue. Four blocks west was Lexington Avenue where a streetcar line ran. I used to take this to 110th Street, transfer to another trolley which took me to Amsterdam Avenue and 138th.

Every morning my mother would hand me a brown paper bag that contained a crisp water roll usually filled with butter. Then she would give me 10 pennies, never nickels or dimes, always pennies. I was painfully self-conscious about the paper bag and would always scrunch it smaller to fit into my pocket. But the pennies were more painful because I always had a feeling the trolley conductor was sneering at me when I handed him the five pennies for the one-way fare.

I was a loner. The only friend I had to t-t-talk to when I was younger and attending P.S. 158 around the corner on Avenue A was Emil Kupec. He was a year ahead of me at school and lived across the street in the house next to Harjes Stable and Coal Yard. I admired him because of his bright, outgoing personality. But then everyone liked him, especially girls.

I wondered why he ever bothered with me, but I learned later that it was because I was a precocious reader. I used to spend most of my time in the small Carnegie Library on Avenue A and 78th Street. I had delved into esoteric literature, struggled with the vedanta, and finally found a book that taught hathayoga.

Emil seldom read anything. He would ask me if I had read a particular book, and if I hadn't I would find it at the library and proudly report on it to him the next day. We used to sit on the wooden pilings along the East River where, alone, I would be able to talk to him easily. I told him about hathayoga and demonstrated some of the exercises. He was so brash that he stood on his head right there on one of the piles. A slight slip would have landed him in the river! After that, I persuaded him to go to a more secluded spot under the hill that became John Jay Park, where we practiced mantra meditation. Then abruptly these meetings ended with his family moving away. It was his last term and after graduation he went on to Jefferson High. The following year I went to Townsend Harris Hall.

We continued to live in the same flat. One day five years later began with the same brown paper bag, the same ten copper pennies, and the same tense lump in my stomach as I started out for Lexington Avenue. I was always careful, after doling out my first five pennies, to place the remaining five in my left-hand pants pocket because there was no hole in it. Noontime found me huddled under the top concrete step of the stadium. The January winds didn't reach me there and I could watch some kids horsing around on the field.

The field isn't there any more. But in those days I frequently went there to eat my roll in isolation. I wished I could join the kids. They were having so much fun. But then, I didn't join anything although I'd been asked to try out for athletics. I rejected all extracurricular activities because I knew it would take money, probably very little, but I didn't have even a little and was ashamed to have to admit it.

Suddenly the clang of a bell brought me out of my reverie. The roll was gone. The kids I'd been watching had disappeared and as I looked toward the heavy Gothic doors I saw them closing. I dashed to my feet, scattering the paper bag and the crumbs, scooped up my books, and flew toward the hall.

There was really no need for my anxiety. I was completely ignored by my instructors. Whether I was in my seat or not, it made no difference. They were all reasonably humane, and, after the first humiliating experience when my name was called the first time, they would not inflict the laughter of the class on my futile attempts to articulate. My last class was over at three and I shuffled out to wait for the trolley. My thoughts kept nagging that I should quit, get a job to earn some money. There was always night school.

The trolley approached, and as always, I waited until the end of the line to get on. I reached into my pocket for the fare, and I went cold. I felt some pennies but all I had was three! In panic I pulled out my pocket. It was true I had only three pennies left. I looked at the conductor in consternation as he pulled the signal cord. The trolley was five blocks away from the stadium when he let me off.

I knew that when I was startled out of my reverie I must have lost those damn pennies. They would probably still be there amid the remains of my lunch. I sighed and began walking back, but just then a Rupert Brewery truck passed, going downtown; so I decided to hitch a ride. I dropped off at 86th Street when the truck slowed for traffic and then walked cross town through Central Park.

I arrived home much later than usual. My mind was made up. I would tell my mother I was going to quit and get a job. I was a little afraid because my mother had been so set on my completing my studies. I waited until after supper. But then I picked up the *Evening Journal* to see if there was a Nell Brinkley drawing. I had some drawing talent and liked to copy them. I turned to the second section but instead of the picture I found a feature story. The headline was a paraphrase: "Every day you're better and better!"

I started to turn the page to go to the comics, disappointed, when my eye was caught up with the name *Emile.* It certainly wasn't a common name, but one fondly familiar to me, so I began to read. The article was about Emile Coué and his lectures. I became fascinated. This was my first introduction to suggestion psychology. Buried in the article was a reference to Coué's book, *Self-Mastery Through Conscious Autosuggestion.*

This moment marked a complete change in my life. The librarian didn't have Coué's book on her shelves but she was able to help me find it in the medical library uptown. I wasn't able to go to any of his lectures but I always got more out of a book than a lecture anyway.

Coué's book introduced me to his teacher, Charcot,

who taught hypnosis to Freud. From then on I devoted every moment of my study time to the writings of Freud, Jung, Adler, finally William James and eventually to Pavlov and the conditioned reflex.

For the first time in my life I had hope. I knew now that my speech mannerism was a conditioned reflex and that it could be reconditioned. I had to learn how to do this. James' introspective psychology helped me find the answer.

Because of my earlier reading in yogic meditation I found myself going into recall quite readily. I began to understand why I had the stutter. I had experienced a feeling of total rejection by my father. I had never had an ego-satisfying father image. I began to understand why my father had become more and more remote, at the very time when I needed and was seeking identity. He ignored me completely. Being a child, I cried. I was admonished. My cries were therefore subdued, repressed. I sobbed silently. Listen to a stutterer – chances are, you'll be listening to repressed sobbing.

Having studied Pavlov I learned how such traumatic experiences, and the emotional responses to them, constitute the causal factor I'd been seeking. It is easy to understand how you can develop a conditioned reflex by the repetition of the stutter.

But knowing all this intellectually didn't bring any catharsis or change in the stutter. Adler gave me the clue I needed. To a child there are only two sides to a coin – love and hate – nothing else. Then, meditating introspectively, I learned how I had begun to hate my father: because I thought he had rejected me.

Here I was, fully grown, still sobbing and stuttering because as a child I had convinced myself that my father had rejected me! James' rationalism helped me to understand. Because I knew how to meditate, I was better able to employ introspection, better able to go back to early incidents in my life. Then, following Freud's free association, I was able to recall repressed material.

For the first time I was able to view my parents in perspective. I began to see my father as a frustrated, henpecked man turning away from his family (and me) because of the sharp criticisms of my mother (whom I had adored). When there was a greater scarcity of money she would snap at my father, grind him down and scathingly reduce him to impotent rage. The image I began to see clearly now was the cathartic material I needed to help me overcome my negative self-image, the image that had me rejected, sobbing for love.

I experienced no magical freedom from my speech mannerism. Having studied Pavlov, I knew I had to recondition my negative self-image by developing a new, positive success image. I began to daydream, to visualize myself as the person I had always wanted to be – poised, confident, assured, a public speaker. I found my formula: I am happy! I have self-confidence! I have self-assurance! I have self-esteem!

Then one day in another classroom, I held up my hand when the instructor asked a question. This was the first time in my life I had had the courage to do this. I could see he was startled to see *my* hand up. He looked for other hands and then nodded to me. I stumbled to my feet and answered loudly and clearly. When I sat down my ears were buzzing and my head felt like a tight balloon. The room seemed unusually silent. They were, I thought, listening to the telltale pounding of my heart!

But then I exulted. I realized that this was my first small success. Suddenly I knew that a series of such small successes would give me the conviction that I had overcome my problem forever.

What followed was a lifetime of study. Every psychology paper or book offered more insight. Slowly I began to formulate the NovaYoga procedure. Then when I discovered Plato's aphorism, "No physician could treat a disease really well until he had it himself," I knew I had developed a viable autogenic technique that could help anyone overcome his hangups.

Chapter **14**

How Alex Relieved His Tensions

THERE IS ONE symptom that is common to every personality problem – tension. The first objective of NovaYoga training is to overcome your tensions. Therefore I will begin these case histories (NovaYoga in action) with *tension*, and an often met psychosomatic response.

Tension kills. Psychosomatic medicine recognizes that while statistics point to heart disease as the greatest killer, it is tension rather than cholesterol that is the primary cause. The heart specialist will tell you of a number of causes for heart failure. Excessive weight, for example, is especially insidious. But what causes a person to overeat? Tension.

Let us review a classic psychosomatic disease – the stomach ulcer. The usual prescription is a bland diet and the advice, "stop worrying." If the patient could stop worrying he wouldn't need the bland diet, because he wouldn't have the ulcer.

What causes tension? Perhaps we ought to examine the word semantically before we attempt to answer the question. The medical dictionary says, "strain, muscular contraction; kinesthetic sensation associated with muscular contraction; a condition of anxiety accompanied by feelings of muscular strain." (Kinesthesia is the innate sensation of muscular movement or presence.)

Thus we know that tension causes muscular contraction. And an autonomic muscular response causes a kinesthetic sensation. It is understood that anxiety (fear) causes an autonomic muscular response. Thus if a situation of stress develops (causing a fear reaction), there is an autonomic physiological response. The viscera is extremely sensitive to emotional stimulus. Fear, for example, causes the endrocrine glands to accelerate their functions and the adrenals pump more sugar into your bloodstream.

It is this increased blood sugar, in the form of glucose, that gives you the energy to fight or flee from the stress-producing stimulus within your environment.

Most people are able to resist unnecessary fear reactions by ignoring, or at least minimizing, the stresses within their environment. But many cannot. They are the ones who, conditioned by early traumatic experiences, overreact because of their subconscious anxiety pattern.

What causes this anxiety pattern? There are a great many possible causes, for example, a person who felt himself rejected as a child, a person who developed feelings of inferiority perhaps due to sibling rivalry, etc. When these persons encounter a situation that seems to parallel their childhood traumatic experiences, their conditioned reflex (anxiety pattern) automatically creates that dictionary definition: "a condition of anxiety accompanied by feelings of muscular strain."

A persistent worrier is probably a person with feelings of insecurity or inadequacy (an underachiever) who is under constant tension because of his worries. He has a conditioned reflex, which is a negative self-image. Subconsciously he sees himself failing, unable to succeed. He experiences almost constantly that kinesthetic sensation because the muscle fibers of his stomach are contracting excessively. (Your stomach muscles so contract when your stomach is empty and you feel pangs of hunger.)

Were you ever so afraid that you had "butterflies in your stomach"? Alas, no butterflies there, but rather a continual contraction of the muscles causing an excess of hydrochloric acid that can attack the glandular tissues of your stomach wall and eventually cause an ulcer.

Your physician therefore gives you excellent advice: "Stop worrying." One physician sent his patient to learn how to relax to stop worrying. NovaYoga didn't treat his stomach ulcer. This was the province of his medical doctor. He was taught the total procedure (which you have read and will now begin to study) to overcome his negative self-image.

The Case History Summary

The summary of each case history given here will follow a pattern. This is the same procedure you will follow when you begin to practice NovaYoga and apply yourself to overcoming your problem. The pattern is as follows:

Case in Point

A brief summation of the person and his problem with sufficient background information to enable you to recognize similar conditioning experiences in yourself should his problem parallel yours.

Introspection. Related to the personality questionnaire which enables you to focus your mind objectively on your symptoms. This will enable you, as it did the person in the case in point, to begin your recall and review your earliest life experiences, trying to find causal factors related to the present problem.

Rationalism. It is important, first, that you understand how your mind functions and how it was conditioned. When you do and when you recall causal factors, you will be able to apply reason and rationalism to such childhood life experiences with adult understanding. You will recognize how closely your mind compares with a computer and how it is that your early life experiences program your computer mind. You will be able to accept the Pavlovian concept of a conditioned reflex and understand why and how it is possible to overcome your personality problem through reconditioning.

Motivation. The drive, that force or power, that spurs you on to accomplish your objective, to overcome your personality problem, your inhibitions, your hangups, and to change your negative self-image to the positive self-image of the person you want to be.

Meditative relaxation. The NovaYoga procedure that enables you to relax in hypnagogic sleep and thus to reach the alpha rhythm, through programmed control of your imaginative faculty and the biofeedback resulting from altered self-imagery.

Autosuggestions. Created to meet your specific needs. However, the ego-expanding suggestions are a must in order to overcome basic feelings of inferiority: "I am happy . . . I have self-confidence . . . self-assurance . . . and self-esteem."

New success image. Based on your motivation; employed to accompany your autosuggestions as well as to guide and spur you to final action in recognizing your small successes, which leads to total conviction, to becoming the person you want to be.

Case in Point

Our first case in point is a man in his late forties whom we shall call Alex. He is single and had a stomach ulcer.

Alex had considerable difficulty accepting NovaYoga philosophy, particularly the Epicurean philosophy of "the moment of reality." However, he was intelligent and determined to follow his doctor's advice, to learn how to relax and thereby stop his worrying. When in a few weeks he began to recognize that he was beginning to learn how to let himself go in meditative relaxation, he simultaneously began to admit that he was beginning to feel better physically as well as mentally. As a result he began to respond more readily to the principles of NovaYoga.

To train him to understand the importance of the moment of reality and to develop his sensual appreciation of the elements within his environment, he was assigned the task of reporting on his observations of everything about him. He had to submit a weekly report of these observations, which included: the beauties of his environment to which he had been totally blind, such as a particularly lovely cloud formation; the variety and beauty of trees in Central Park, of which he had been oblivious; of birds he now saw for the first time; and of people – all types and characters, and girls whom he had shut out of his life completely.

He thought this procedure silly at first, but soon took pleasure in it. He reported on different tastes he was able to discern despite the limited diet his doctor had prescribed, so that he began to appreciate and take pleasure in sharpened taste sensations. He soon took widened interest in everything outside himself, and gradually his outlook changed. He then eagerly accepted the premise of the moment of reality, recognizing that he had never before been able to savor his life experience.

His attitude toward persons he met daily changed to greater tolerance. He learned to laugh at jokes, and then at himself. He was learning how his increased sensuality was teaching him the simple pleasures of life for the very first time.

Introspection. Revealed an unhappy childhood. His parents had separated when he was nine years old. His mother struggled to keep her family together, he and an older sister. He recalled the poverty and many incidents which made him feel that his mother favored his sister. He never received any tactile assurance of love, didn't know what it meant to be hugged and kissed or told he was wonderful and that he was loved. His mother made him work at all kinds of menial jobs, reminding him that his sister was working and contributing more to the family's welfare than he was. He felt rejected, first by his father and then by his mother. His feelings of insecurity were compounded by deep-seated feelings of inferiority due to sibling rivalry.

Rationalism. He was able eventually to understand the severe problems his mother faced trying to keep her family intact. While she was undemonstrative she proved her deep love for him by going to work in a clothing sweatshop and forcing his sister to work, as well, in order to support him. Such rationalization enabled him to feel love for his mother (and for his sister) which he had never been able to do before. He accepted also the explanation that his sister was indeed able to provide more than he, for the simple and obvious reason that she was older and therefore more capable than he could be expected to be.

Motivation. This was at first a little difficult to establish. He was now fully mature. His mother was dead. His sister had married and had two children whom he ignored in his capacity of uncle. The older child, a boy, was now in high school and despaired of college because his mother was a widow and didn't have the means to continue his education. He accepted my suggestion that he "adopt" this boy, that is, help the boy to avoid the hardships he himself had endured.

Meditative relaxation. Based on the basic beach-relaxation image. However, to bolster his motivation, the imagery included his nephew. Both he and his nephew were lying on the blanket, the boy in deep physiological sleep while he visualized himself in deep hypnagogic sleep.

Autosuggestions. "I am happy, I have self-confidence, self-assurance, and self-esteem!" This was repeated three times before he lapsed into normal, natural physiological sleep. In the morning, on awakening, he would say to himself, while still in bed: "Every day in every way I am better and better!"

New success image. Based on his motivation. He visualized himself attending his nephew's college graduation. He had provided the means. He was prouder at this moment than at any time in his whole life – and he was free of his ulcer!

COMMENT

Most subjects are reasonably ready to accept NovaYoga principles and practices. However, this subject was extremely inhibited by his early traumatic experiences.

For him to learn how to let himself go, it was necessary to change his materialistic philosophy, his greed, his limited sensuality by accepting the moment of reality. Such a philosophy is probably equally important to you, with your own problem, as it was with him. Be sure you study it, that you understand it, and that you practice it.

Chapter **15**

How Bill Overcame His Feelings of Inferiority

THE MOST COMMON personality problem NovaYoga has been called on to deal with is the inhibitory characteristics of the underachiever. There are so many of us who are living and working below the level of our competence that it would appear that almost everyone has feelings of inferiority in some area.

When you are programmed with negative life experiences during your childhood, experiences that caused you to feel rejected perhaps, or you somehow got the impression that your brother (or sister) was favored and hence you began to feel yourself unworthy, it is then that you very probably began to develop feelings of inferiority. The subliminal image that is created as a result of your life experiences is either a negative self-image or, if you are one of the rare fortunate ones, a positive self-image. If it is the former, you automatically expect to fail, to be rejected by persons and/or circumstances within your social or business environment.

You need only to look around you to see how widespread this problem is. You undoubtedly know persons, either socially or in business, who are authority figures, bosses who are employing others. How many such bosses, to your knowledge or in your opinion, are as capable, smart, clever, or even intelligent as some of the men they employ? Perhaps you (if you compare yourself with your boss) feel that you are better equipped, have more talent, more ability, more intelligence, are in many ways superior to him.

Why, then, is he not working for you, rather than the other way around? Possibly you will say that it's just dumb luck or simply that he's got the kind of nerve, chutzpah, that enables him to bully his way ahead at the expense of others. You may defend yourself by saying "I've never had the opportunities he's had!" or, "He's too dumb to see that his way of thinking is all wrong! I'm the one who has to straighten things out; make them work!"

And you may be absolutely right! You may indeed be smarter, more competent, more capable than he. But you haven't explained yet why he is *your* boss.

Perhaps you don't know. Yet the answer is quite simple. It is most likely because, despite his ineptness, his lack of talent and ability, he has something you haven't. He has self-confidence, self-assurance, and self-esteem.

This doesn't mean, simply, that he feels superior while you feel inferior. It means that while he is not inhibited by feelings of inferiority, you are!

If you are not inhibited by such feelings then you are one of those rare persons whose early life experiences has nurtured within you a positive self-image *which is the motivating force for that wonderful feeling of self-confidence, self-assurance, and self-esteem.*

To illustrate this personality problem, I have chosen, out of literally hundreds, a case history that follows a somewhat "classic" pattern: early life-experiences that conditioned a person to feelings of inferiority despite loving parents.

There were three children in Bill's family. He was

the middle child. Now don't leap to any conclusions – such as, a middle child will always develop feelings of inferiority. Unfortunately for Bill, he faced a tough situation. His older brother was domineering and his younger sister was sickly, virtually an invalid. A situation such as this usually results in an environment in which the middle child receives few tactile demonstrations of love, much less than his hard-hitting older brother who forcibly made demands for attention, while his sickly sister automatically claimed most of the attention and tactile expressions of love their mother could provide.

Often, as in this situation, the middle child simply "gives up," becomes passive, develops a negative self-image because of feelings of unworthiness, and hence, feels inferior.

However, there's another side to this coin. Because of the severe competition, this middle person can become excessively aggressive and eventually compulsively so, making severe demands on everyone around him and even greater demands on himself.

In this case, the young man accepted the passive role and developed deep-seated feelings of inferiority. It would do you well to study this case history, whether your problem is similar or not, because it effectively demonstrates how the NovaYoga procedure can be applied to your problem.

Case in Point

The case in point is that of a young black man whom I will call Bill. He worked as a male nurse. (Actually he was a nurse's aide.) He sought help from NovaYoga because he felt unhappy about being inferior to the doctors and medical technicians from whom he had to take orders. He felt he was a "nobody."

Introspection. Brought out many early life experiences in the Panamanian village where he lived with an older brother, a younger sister, and his parents. He disliked (although he envied) his older brother because he was "bossy," domineering, overwhelming. He liked his younger sister who was sickly and who therefore claimed most of their mother's attention. He adjusted to his situation by becoming submissive.

Rationalization. When he developed an intellectual understanding of his early life situation, he was able to rationalize his present feelings in the light of the parallel feelings he experienced as a child. He could accept the idea that his present unhappiness was similiar to the unhappiness he experienced as a child, that his dislike of his professional superiors was exactly parallel to his dislike of his (superior) brother. His present wish to change his situation was, again, parallel to his emigrating to the United States.

Motivation. The positive self-image that was created, based on his powerful drive to attain recognition as an individual, as well as an ego-satisfying status. He had, however, no idea how he could alter his present inferior status. When it was pointed out that he had the ability of becoming a medical technician, he accepted with great enthusiasm the suggestion that he study physical therapy. As a physiotherapist he felt himself in an ego-satisfying position.

Meditative relaxation. Speedily attained because of his vivid recollection of how he took care of his younger sister, cradling her in his strong arms and gently massaging her forehead until she slept. Then he would relax himself and drift into sleep, holding her in his arms as others do with a Teddy bear.

Autosuggestions. "I am happy! I have self-confidence, self-assurance, and self-esteem – because I am a physiotherapist!" He would repeat these, following meditative relaxation, every night as he drifted off into normal, natural, physiological sleep.

New success image. Based on his motivation. He saw himself as a physiotherapist gently but powerfully massaging his sister's body, feeling her become well, feeling proud of himself as a successful physiotherapist.

COMMENT

The NovaYoga postulate is that you are "programmed" by your life experiences. This is a conditioning which has the effect of creating either a negative or positive self-image. If your subliminal self-image is negative, if therefore you allow yourself only the passive, secondary, perhaps subservient, role, you have developed a self-image of unworthiness and inferiority. Pavlov demonstrated that it is possible to recondition this negative self-image to a positive self-image which will become your motivational drive to become the person you want to be. This case history is a simple yet effective demonstration of this procedure.

Chapter 16

How Cathy Overcame Her Frustrations

THE REASONS FOR one's feelings of frustration are readily understood, if not readily overcome. The first illustration that comes to mind is an expression I heard about an editor I know: "He's a frustrated writer." What this remark implied was that this person was forced to do editorial work, whereas his inner drive urged him to become a writer, hence his feelings of frustration.

Similar remarks may be said of anyone who is doing one thing while his impulse is to do another. This would apply to the salesman who wants to be a painter, the accountant who'd prefer to sell, the mechanic who likes to keep records, the secretary who wants to keep house, the butcher, the baker, the candlestick-maker – all want to be someone or something else.

From time to time everyone feels frustrated if the thing he wants is denied him. These problems of individual frustrations are easily understood and may be resolved by simple recognition and action. If my editor friend wants to write more than anything else, then he writes! Or so it would appear. If everyone could recognize the cause of his frustration, he could solve his problem by simply acting on that recognition.

The real problem of frustration, however, lies with the person who cannot recognize the cause and who subconsciously seeks out those situations within his environment that will inevitably result in his being frustrated. To illustrate this problem I have chosen as a case in point a girl by the name of Cathy who experienced frustration virtually every time she tried to please someone.

Meditative introspection brought to her recall an early experience that proved to be a causal factor contributing to understanding her present feelings of constant frustration.

The incident she recalled happened to her when she was a little under two years old (remarkable recall). She saw herself in a playpen. Her mother had given her a glass of milk to drink. She sipped the milk and then, as the playpen was alongside a table, she tried to reach up to place the glass on it. She was too little. The glass slipped and fell to the floor of her playpen, spilling all the milk.

Her mother became angry and reached down and spanked her. The girl's recollection was remarkable. She was able to recall that in her mind she was trying to express to her mother that she was only trying to please her. She remembered, as she cried from the spanking, that she was thinking that she wasn't a bad girl, that she meant to be good.

Spurred by this unusual glimpse into her early childhood she was able to recall other, later, incidents that had had a similar effect. She had attempted many times to please her mother, with just the opposite effect and with the resulting punishment.

She was not able to recall if she had ever grown to hate her mother. It was difficult for her to accept such an idea. Nevertheless, she did accept the idea that as a small child there were only two sides to the coin – love and hate. If her mother constantly displayed her displeasure with her, it certainly wasn't love.

Once she was able to understand how a small child *could* develop hatred for her mother, she was able to accept the idea that feelings of guilt could result from the ensuing conflict with her superego, her moral guide, and censor. If circumstances develop which cause feelings of hate rather than love, the ensuing conflict may result in repressed feelings of guilt. Punishment can take the form of constantly repeated frustrations.

Case in Point

This case in point is a girl named Cathy. She was 24 at the time. When she came to NovaYoga, her problem was that she was unable to establish a satisfactory relationship with anyone she loved or with whom she wanted to be friendly. Her attempts would invariably result in frustration. She was rebuffed every time she tried to please her boss, her boy friend, or her mother. She had been sharply criticized by her boss, bringing her to tears. She lost her boy friend after a painful scene in which he reproached her. The idea that she was being punished didn't occur to her, but such repeated frustrations were beyond her understanding.

Introspection. Brought to her all the details of those incidents. At first she thought she was merely misunderstood because her good intentions seemed always to cause disappointment and frustration. Her earlier recollections, however, revealed to her that she was indeed a child of an exceedingly demanding mother. It became apparent to her that her mother made excessive, neurotic demands on her as a child. Her mother was not satisfied with anything the girl did to please her. Cathy had an *impression* that her mother was very loving, although she had no firm recollection of any tactile demonstrations of love. She could not recall a single instance of her mother hugging or praising her.

Rationalization. Enabled her to accept the fact of her mother's neuroticism. She recognized that, while her mother did love her in her strange way, she was totally unable to demonstrate this love in a normal manner that would have been satisfying to the child's ego. With adult rationalism she was able to forgive her mother and found that then she had a compassionate understanding and was able to love her mother with greater sympathy.

Motivation. Was strongly established when she made a decision to change her pattern of living. She made arrangements to move into an apartment with a girl friend. She soon came to realize that she was happier living apart from her mother and pursuing her own life. This was a maturing experience. Because of it, she readily accepted the suggestion that she was able to understand and love her mother with toleration as she grew more independent and self-assured.

Meditative relaxation. Based on her love of swimming and the beach. She was trained to visualize herself lying on a blanket, her eyes closed in hypnagogic sleep, with the sound of the waves and seagulls to lull her into that relaxed state when she experienced the alpha rhythm.

Autosuggestions. "I am happy! I have self-confidence, self-assurance and self-esteem!" She accepted the idea that these suggestions would build up her ego image and give her an assertive chutzpah, to overcome her sensitivity with resultant frustration feelings. She would be able to reduce any future frustrations to the level of simple annoyances, which her chutzpah could ignore.

New success image. She visualized this while giving herself the autosuggestion of her mother embracing her – her mother finally approving of her, her mother finally loving her.

COMMENT

Frustrations may easily become a conditioned reflex. Every simple annoyance can be magnified into a giant frustration. The detachment you can achieve when you have practiced meditative relaxation and finally Nova-Yoga mantra meditation can help you overcome all frustrating experiences by making you impervious to emotional distraction. Meditators practice long and patiently just to attain that mental state of serenity and detachment. You will also be able to reach this state if you overcome your negative self-image – as Cathy did.

Chapter 17

How Dora Conquered Her Sexual Hangup

THE KINSEY REPORT was the first, but there have been many others since, including the extensive data accumulated by the research team of Masters and Johnson, to indicate that the primary cause for divorce in this country is sexual incompatibility.

When the emerging adult, either male or female, is unable to adjust satisfactorily to the sexual experience and discover the deeply satisfying emotional satisfaction that should result, it is not necessarily true that one is impotent or frigid. It is more often the direct result of negative conditioning.

The case in point chosen to illustrate how NovaYoga can train the individual to make proper adjustment was an attractive young brunette who was so desperately unhappy that she cried almost incessantly when she was alone with her thoughts. She was at college and shared a room with her boy friend. They planned to marry as soon as they could after graduation and after they were able to get jobs.

She was deeply in love, but daily she became more

fearful about their relationship. He was a bold, powerful lover, perhaps a little too aggressive. She had been unable to derive any pleasure from these experiences. She had never achieved orgasm and was convinced that she was innately frigid and incapable of expressing her love physically.

The first approach to her problem was a physical examination. Her physician advised her that she was completely normal and that there was absolutely no organic basis for her inability to reach climax. Her doctor told her that in his opinion she was too tense and that she should learn to relax.

Introspection revealed that her mother was unusually biased against sex. As a small child and all through her puberty she was able to recall that her mother passionately inveighed against all references to sex. In retrospect it appeared evident that her mother was determined to deny all sexual impulses. Nevertheless, her recall brought her many pleasant memories of her mother and of her love.

She knew her father very little because he traveled and was home infrequently. When he was home, there were frequent scenes of bickering between her parents that disturbed her. Totally committed to her mother, she disliked her father at first and later came to fear him.

Her mother had placed her in a convent school in preparation for college, but when she finally left home to attend college she was unable to cope with her new freedom. She was frightened. Gradually she adjusted and began to overcome her shyness by taking part in her girl friends' frank discussions of sex.

It was extremely difficult, even painful, but she knew it was part of growing up. Eventually she began to think herself enlightened and began to double date. These early dating experiences were difficult because of her shyness. Eventually she met and fell in love with a boy and in her second year at college decided to live with him.

She reveled, at first, in what she thought was her final maturing. She felt herself unshackled – free! But as time went on, this "freedom" brought her only misery. Her boy friend was obviously deeply in love with her, and she couldn't bring herself to speak of her unhappiness. She found herself hating all love play and was now bickering with her boy friend. She would cry at the smallest provocation. Finally, because of her fear of losing her boy friend, she sought help from her physician, and, acting on his advice that she learn how to relax, she came to study NovaYoga.

Case in Point

A college student whom I will call Dora was deeply in love but had reached a point in her relationship with her boy friend that she despaired of marriage. Although her physician had assured her there was no organic basis for her problem and that she was too tense, she began to convince herself that she had inherited her frigid attitude and feared that she might be a latent homosexual. Still, she was deeply in love, had sexual desire, and wanted to be loved very much. She was ecstatically happy with her boy friend at first, but when she was unable to achieve orgasm she began to loathe herself as well as all sexual expression.

Introspection. Revealed a background of early conditioning by her mother who apparently had a phobia about sex. She was programmed very early to regard all sexual expression as evil, dirty, something to be shunned. The girl was sent to a convent school where discipline was extremely strict and all reference to sex proscribed. The girl accepted the idea that sex was a necessary burden placed on all women as a result of the act of Eve in disobeying the edict against tasting of the fruit of the tree of knowledge.

Rationalization. Enabled her to overcome the emotional effects of her early conditioning because of her understanding now of how she had been programmed. She was able to reconcile her feelings toward both her father and mother because of her adult experiences. She recognized her mother's unnatural attitude toward sex and with understanding forgave her mother and was thus able to completely overcome the negative self-image that was the cause of her tensions and her inability to let herself go in a sexual relationship.

Motivation. Was based on her love for her boy friend and her newfound ability to let herself go as she learned to overcome her tensions. Now that she was able to accept the idea that she was perfectly normal, she could esteem herself as a fitting companion and wife capable of making a happy home and life together.

Meditative relaxation. Was enhanced by the fact that her boy friend was an expert swimmer on the swimming team and therefore extremely fond of water. She was able to visualize herself, with him at her side, lying on a beach lapsing into hypnagogic sleep and attaining the alpha rhythm.

Autosuggestions. "I am happy! I have self-confidence, self-assurance, and self-esteem – because Ted loves me!"

New success image. Her new self-image was of herself and her boy friend. They were on an isolated beach lying on a blanket. The sun was bright, the air was warm, and she was looking up into his eyes as he gently fondled her, feeling herself completely filled with peace and love.

COMMENT:

Aside from the personal details of this case history, it is a pattern that can be repeated in many, many instances of sexual hangups. How many women are getting little or no pleasure from their experiences because of deeply repressed feelings of guilt, perhaps which prevent them from "letting themselves go"? How many men are made virtually impotent because of some early conditioning that created a negative self-image? Remember Coué's statement that suggestions (based on your self-image) can kill you or save your life.

Chapter 18

How Eva Cured Her Insomnia

ONE OF THE prime requisites of the modern advertising man is creativity. He must have a well-developed and controlled imaginative faculty. For example, in promoting a sleep-inducing tablet on television, one that may be purchased without prescription, an advertising man came up with a novel suggestion. He proposed that our brain is equipped with a "sleep center" and that by taking one or more of the tablets he was promoting, this sleep center could be induced to "shut down" for the night.

Wouldn't it be wonderful if this were the case. All anyone suffering from insomnia would have to do is to take a tablet and sleep. Of course it is true that your physician could prescribe barbiturates, which would certainly put you to sleep. The fact that you know this helps the advertising man sell his idea of a sleep center to you.

Actually the idea of a sleep center is not far off. Nature has provided a means of forcing rest in order that your body can recoup expended energy. We call this rest sleep. Under ordinary circumstances, when your body calls for rest, you usually lie down and sleep.

What actually happens when we stop our activity,

mental and physical, and lie down to get this rest? Normally, we suspend our critical faculty and drift off into hypnagogic sleep as soon as this critical faculty becomes quiescent, then into alpha and on down to theta, and finally hit the bottom with delta rhythm. You are already familiar with this state of consciousness because if you trained yourself to meditative relaxation, you did precisely the same: drifted into hypnagogic sleep and the alpha rhythm. The only difference is that you were kept in that altered state of consciousness, between the alpha and theta rhythms.

What happens when this process doesn't function as it is supposed to? You lie there in bed fighting to go to sleep, and the harder you fight the further away does the sleep state of delta go. You've got to relax. And how do you relax? You ought to know by now. You control the flow of your thoughts; you control your imagery; you control your imaginative faculty. One of the best ways to do this is, of course, the meditative relaxation procedure you were taught.

Our brain, of course, never stops functioning. When it does, you won't know or care because you'll be dead. Since sleep is a biological necessity, considerable research has been done with the electroencephalograph. While there is still much that is not known about the mechanism, it does appear that dreaming is vital. If you are prevented from having dreams while you sleep, you become extremely irritable. If your dream mechanism is interrupted for a period of days (or nights) it can affect the functioning of your mind. Brainwashing techniques employ such procedures to force the individual to accept ideas he would otherwise have refuted.

It appears that the sleep procedure allows the conscious area, the critical faculty, to become quiescent only to stop thinking about reality in order to turn inward to contemplate your psychic world and enter your dream life. Everybody dreams during sleep, even those who claim they don't. Your dream periods are manifested in REMs (rapid eye movements).

But what about the person who wants to sleep but can't. One reason might be that there's some stress-producing circumstances within your environment that you are struggling with and cannot let go long enough to relax. You toss and toss, going over the same treadmill, until through sheer exhaustion your body rebels and forces you to sleep.

Another reason may be that there is something within your subconscious mind you are afraid to confront in your dreams, some long-repressed traumatic material perhaps. It could be something that causes feelings of guilt, and you are reluctant to be reminded of this emotional problem. In either case, the problem is emotional and hence falls within the purview of NovaYoga.

The case in point should be fairly typical – a young married woman who was undergoing treatment with a clinical psychologist who referred her to NovaYoga for conditioning to overcome her insomnia.

Case in Point

An attractive married woman in her early forties was taking family counsel from a clinical psychologist for problems within her immediate family home environment with which she was having difficulty coping.

Introspection. Speedily achieved because of the woman's experience with the clinical psychologist. She was nervous and tense. She was able to realize the reason because her present home environment closely paralleled early childhood experiences – when she had been subjected to constant fear and tension. Her fears as a child were realized when her home was broken up by the divorce of her parents. She dreaded the possibility of the same thing happening to her.

Rationalization. She was able to recognize that she was overreacting to her present situation because of her early *conditioned* fear of a broken home. Therefore she was able to rationalize her early experience with sufficient adult objectivity, that whereas as a child she had no opportunity to alter the situation, now as an adult she did; since her motivations were based on her overriding desire to spare her children the pain of her own experiences, she could and would act maturely.

Motivation. Strengthened because of her strong love for her children and her desire to provide a loving, stress-free environment to assure normal development and happiness for her children.

Meditative relaxation. A bit difficult at first. She couldn't accept beach relaxation because such a scene related to unhappy incidents in her childhood. She was trained, instead, to another scene: walking through a lovely wooded glade toward two tall oak trees near a sparkling lake. There was a hammock stretched between the two trees. She slipped into the hammock, felt it holding her as though in a tight embrace as she stretched contentedly, feeling the hammock sway gently back and forth, back and forth. She closed her eyes and sighed in peace as she felt a faint breeze from off the lake. The slow, drowsy movement of the hammock, like the gentle rocking of a cradle, relaxed her completely as she repeated the phrase, "I am at peace, fully relaxed."

Autosuggestions. "I am happy! I am safe! My family is safe!" She would repeat this in a slow, drowsy manner, feeling more and more relaxed as she did so . . . and gradually she would slip into sleep.

New success image. She employed this in conjunction with the autosuggestions: each night, on retiring to her lovely bedroom decorated with frilly, feminine, pink curtains, she would close her eyes, visualize this room in softly, subdued light with the door ajar. Then, concentrating on this door, she would see it move slowly, closing, closing, closing, and when it was closed she knew her family was safe, she was safe, and so she could sleep.

COMMENT:

Normally anyone suffering from insomnia would find the answer in meditative relaxation. A tape of the relaxation procedure is a virtual guarantee of sleep. In this case, however, the young woman was having to fight to hold her family together, and fortunately family counseling was enabling her to accomplish this. Her fears meanwhile caused her insomnia, which was affecting her health. For this reason her therapist sent her to learn the relaxation technique. If your problem is parallel to hers, perhaps a dynamic self-image such as the one that meant so much to her could mean as much to you.

Chapter 19

How Frank and George Quit Smoking for Good

"WHAT WILL PEOPLE say?" You've heard this many times. Perhaps you've said it yourself many times. Why? Are you concerned about people's opinions? Yes, you are. Your whole life style is determined by what you think others will think of you.

This is especially true when you are quite young. You want desperately to be like everyone else in your group. It is enormously important that you be accepted, that you become one of the group. This is what is called *peer pressure*.

The best example of this pressure and what it can do to you is the current drug scene. Why, when the horrors of drugs have been portrayed – the degradation, the sheer, wanton waste of life – do young people allow themselves to be sucked into the frightful maelstrom that can lead them into a life of unspeakable misery?

Peer pressure.

A number of excellent motion pictures have clearly shown the insidious power of this pressure. The young girl, new to the community, self-conscious, timid, longing for acceptance, is suddenly invited to join a group. She is thrilled that at last she is going to make friends, that she will no longer be lonely, that she will be accepted.

You know, of course, what happens. The group meets to smoke pot; she is offered a joint. Can she refuse? Of course she can, but will she? The chances are, she will not, that she will take a drag, then another and pretend that she is enjoying herself, that she is one of the group.

The rest has become a cliché. When pot palls, there's speed, and acid, and finally someone slips in H. The complete moral degradation follows, the least of which is prostitution. Peer pressure.

If peer pressure is so potent a force, then you can understand why cigarette smoking is constantly on the increase despite all the publicity, even government pressure, trying to stem the tide. While they are bad enough, cigarettes are fortunately among the least of the tributes the individual (the unfulfilled individual) may be called on to pay to peer pressure.

Eventually many adults reach a decision, for one reason or another, that they will quit smoking. They try, and they fail because, by the time they have reached such a decision, their smoking habit has become a conditioned reflex.

By now you should know something about conditioned reflexes. It means simply that the habit has become subconsciously motivated and the stimulus is *tension*. You reach – entirely automatically – for your package of cigarettes whenever you experience subliminal tension. "Hold on!" you say, "Maybe I smoke because of tension – sometimes, but I'm sure there are many, many times I smoke simply because I like to."

Don't kid yourself. I said you smoke because of *subliminal* tension. That means even that cigarette you light up after a satisfying meal, that cigarette that tastes so good (I'm certainly not tense then!). Try *not* to smoke after that satisfying meal. How do you feel? Nervous?

Jittery? Of course! You've *habituated* yourself to that after-dinner cigarette, and the moment you stop eating, you start developing tension in anticipation of that cigarette! It's become a ritual, a habit, a conditioned reflex.

The reason the NovaYoga technique is so effective in helping persons overcome their cigarette-smoking habits is that it is, first, a technique that trains you to overcome your tensions. But it isn't always easy. The reason I began this case history by speaking of drugs is that cigarettes are a form of addiction – somewhat milder, thank goodness – but still there are going to be some withdrawal pains. That is, most subjects experience withdrawal pains. There are some who don't, some who are able to accept and follow Adler's dictum, "All that is necessary is that you obey . . . [then magic happens]." That's why this case history is a doubleheader. One describes an instantaneous remission and the other the struggle with withdrawal symptoms.

Case in Point—Frank

Frank was in his early thirties and worked as a hair stylist. He had smoked since his teens and now wanted to give up the habit. When asked why, he said, "Well, I don't like it . . . it smells bad, it even tastes bad."

If you actually dislike it, he was asked, why don't you just stop?

"I can't! I find myself reaching for the package in between appointments. I've nothing else to do!"

The fact was evident that he had conditioned himself to smoking, as the thing he had to do when he had nothing else to do.

He was given all the material that appears in the first two chapters. He accepted all the principles, especially the moment of reality. When he was trained in meditative relaxation he responded exactly as Alder would have wanted. He went into a deep trance and relaxed as he had never been able to do before. He was given no suggestions about his smoking. The only suggestions were that he would respond to the meditative relaxation procedure more and more as he repeated it and that he would accept astral projection as a deepening technique, to bring him to a sublime altered state of consciousness.

His next session consisted only of training in astral projection. He was given his success image and suggestions, as follows:

> You will visualize your bathroom . . . you are standing in front of the john . . . the seat is up and you are crumpling your *last* package of cigarettes . . . there are still some cigarettes in the package, but you have made your decision . . . you are tearing up this package of cigarettes . . . you tear up everything into little bits and pieces . . . you drop them into the toilet bowl . . . you can see the torn bits of paper and the torn bits of cigarettes floating on the water . . . now you flush the bowl . . . you watch the water as it swirls around and around. . . . As the paper and cigarettes flush down the drain, you say to yourself: "There goes my cigarette-smoking habit!" You have disliked the taste of cigarettes . . . and now you are glad that you will never taste another . . . if you ever put another cigarette to your lips the taste will be so bad that it will actually make you ill . . . you will *not* smoke another cigarette—ever!

And he never did. He had three subsequent sessions to train him in NovaYoga mantra meditation and to reinforce the suggestions given, with the added suggestion that the meditative training would free him of all tension and hence of any possible temptation to resume the filthy habit of smoking. Being an unusually apt subject, he was able to discard his conditioned reflex with this single suggestion and imagery and attain that detached state of serenity which comes with practiced facility in mantra meditation.

Case in Point—George

George was an older man, now in his sixties, who had smoked ever since he was 11 years old. He worked as a chauffeur. He smoked as many as three packs of cigarettes a day, mostly because of idleness. Most of his time was spent waiting for his employer. His only pastimes were listening to the car radio and smoking. His decision to stop smoking came as a result of the anti-smoking programs he heard on the radio.

Introspection. Necessary, because, unlike Frank, he was unresponsive to the relaxation technique. He was, however, able to recall incidents as a child in his native Sweden. He took up smoking to achieve status with a group of youngsters, all somewhat older than he, with whom he wanted to play. He had some difficulty understanding this as peer pressure but did admit that he wouldn't have started smoking if it hadn't been for the other boys – he wanted to be like them.

Rationalization. Since he didn't have a similiar group with whom he had to maintain status, he admitted that there was no longer a compelling reason for continuing to smoke. He felt he would be more admired (gain greater status) by his present friends if he could demonstrate his ability to quit the habit while many of his friends couldn't.

Motivation. Often the only (and certainly the most powerful) force to spur the subject to attain his success image. His remark that he felt he would be admired if he were to succeed quitting *while many of his friends couldn't* was the basis for the suggestions used to support his success image. More probing uncovered a fact that he hadn't mentioned. One of his friends had died recently from emphysema; he had been a heavy smoker. Without using this fact as a threat, the subject's impression that his friend's death was connected with his smoking was reinforced, because he did not want to die of emphysema.

Meditative relaxation. An excellent image was suggested because of his life in Sweden, where he had been able to take a steam bath and then roll in the snow. He recalled the exquisite physical state of well-being he experienced after the snow rubdown and was lying on a cot covered with a thin blanket, sleeping. This image he interpreted as an image of health and strength (of character).

Autosuggestions. "I am happy! I am healthy! I no longer smoke!" He repeated these suggestions as he watched his new success image.

New success image. He would visualize himself in the steam bath, rolling in the snow, getting a rubdown – then refusing a cigarette but accepting a bag of peanuts!

COMMENTS:

These twin case histories were quoted as an instance of a simple behavioristic procedure (if you are totally receptive), compared with a more arduous and time-consuming introspective approach. Both procedures are effective. The behavioristic approach should be tried with confidence. One approach is known as a "cold turkey" quitting, whereas the other is a gradual withdrawal, as follows: he is required to start by taking five cigarettes from a package, crumbling them and dropping them in the toilet bowl, saying, "There goes my cigarette smoking habit!" 10 the next day, 15 the third, and so on until on the fourth day he is discarding a whole pack. Thus every four days he discards a package of cigarettes and so in 12 days he overcomes his last of three daily packs! Meanwhile he had consumed four pounds of peanuts, convinced of his great strength of character and improved health.

Chapter 20

How Helen Stopped Her Compulsive Eating and Became Thin

I HAVE WAITED until this chapter before touching on the subject of your biochemistry. NovaYoga focuses on your mental acuity by training you to control your *imaginative faculty.* But for optimum results it is necessary that you attain optimum health and that therefore all the organs within your body – particularly your brain, the organ of imagination – attain optimum health.

In the past decade we have seen a virtual revolution within the medical profession. Nutrition is at long last being recognized as vital. Many books have appeared, as well as technical papers, stating the importance of vitamins and minerals. I will list only a few of those whose focus is on the mind: A. Hoffer, M.D., "Biochemistry of Nicotinic Acid and Nicotinamide," *Psychosomatics,* vol. 8, 1967; and with Humphrey Osmond, M.D., "A Comprehensive Theory of Schizophrenia," *Int. Journal of Psychiatry,* vol. 2, no. 4 (both are pioneers in megavitamin therapy); Linus Pauling, Ph.D., *Vitamin C and the Common Cold,* and with David Hawkins, M.D., *Orthomolecular Psychiatry,* W. H. Freeman, Pub.; George Watson, Ph.D., *Nutrition and Your Mind,* Harper & Row; and

Henry G. Bieler, M.D., *Food Is Your Best Medicine,* Random House.

To express the problem of your total health simply, think of your body as a machine, an extremely complex machine that combines the functions of a computer, a programmer, and a motor. The first provides the energy, the second provides the control, and the third provides the physical means to respond to such energized control.

For this infinitely complex mechanism to function properly there is required an equally complex fuel system. Chief among the ingredients of this fuel system is oxygen. Without it nothing happens. With it your body can function if it is fueled additionally with proper nutriment. This nutriment must consist of proteins, fats, and carbohydrates, which must provide the proper amount and balance of vitamins and minerals. If your body is normal, that is, if it can properly metabolize and absorb from this nutriment all the chemical ingredients required by your body and its organs, then your body will possess what could be said is a normal capacity to act and react in a normal manner within your environment.

It is when you are *not* normal, however, when your body chemistry is off balance due perhaps to an organic inability to manufacture or utilize certain chemicals or when you deliberately alter your protein-fat-carbohydrate intake so that you supply your body with an abnormal fuel regimen, that this marvelous mechanism, your body, begins to malfunction.

Malfunction can take any of the forms discussed in the case histories given, or it can take the form of *obesity,* which is the subject of this chapter.

A common symptom of a hangup is obesity, plain overweight. Except for the very rare cases of glandular or metabolic imbalance, the reason you become fat is that you eat too much, especially of the wrong foods. You know very well why you are overweight and yet you probably cannot do anything about it. At least, that's what you *think*. The fact is, you can do something about it. The fact that you're studying NovaYoga is evidence that you *are* doing something about it.

The first thing you must acknowledge is that you have become a compulsive eater. You eat not to satisfy your hunger but to satisfy a subliminal hangup.

The causal factor of this hangup of yours will always be found in the programming or conditioning you received as a child. In one case a 269-pound man of 32 learned that his compulsive eating habit stemmed from his feelings of rejection when a small child. In another case a young woman become excessively obese because she had a boy friend and was about to be married. Introspection revealed that when she was a child her mother frequently complained to her about her father and often remarked, "You'll be better off not married!"

The case in point was a blond, attractive, witty young woman by the name of Helen. She was five feet four inches tall and weighed 185 pounds. She had previously tried a Weight Watchers diet and lost 50 pounds. But here she was back again, and climbing.

Case in Point

Helen was an attractive young woman who buried herself in huge layers of fat. She thought her problem was glandular, although her doctor told her that she was perfectly normal – merely overweight. She then tried to convince herself that it was heredity because her mother had always been plump.

Introspection. Revealed some interesting facts. First, she had recently lost her boy friend, and this had triggered her latest binge of overeating sweets and carbohydrates. Earlier recall, however, revealed a conditioning pattern.

When she was little, her mother always gave her rewards in the form of sweets – cake and cookies – or to stop a tantrum. Further, her mother was undemonstrative. She never hugged or kissed the child to tell her how much she was loved; instead she handed out sweets.

Rationalization. Enabled her to recognize that sweets and carbohydrates had become tokens of love. They had become the symbols of the loving attention she craved as a child. She accepted this as the cause of her compulsion to eat sweets when triggered by some situation within her environment such as losing her boy friend. She turned automatically to sweets to satisfy her craving for love.

Motivation. Based on her rationalization of her craving for love. She was able to accept and be motivated by the idea that at 125 pounds she would be far better able to attract men. Her motivation became stronger when she determined to get a new boy friend – to show up her former one.

Meditative relaxation. The beach scene, because she recalled an incident that happened when she was a child. She was at a beach with her mother and father who struck up an acquaintance with another family they met next to where they had put down their blanket. The other family had a son about the same age, and she recalled how happy she felt when both mothers had the children lie down together on the blanket to rest and sleep.

Autosuggestions. "I am happy! I weigh 125 pounds! He loves me!" repeated over and over, until she drifted off into a normal, natural physiological sleep.

New success image. Now a lovely 125-pound woman wearing a daring bikini on the same beach, lying on a blanket alongside one of the young men from her office she wanted to attract. In the background was her former boy friend looking at her with longing and envious eyes. She saw herself glancing covertly at her former boy friend and reveling in her triumph. She then turned to her new boy friend and lay down beside him.

COMMENT:

Motivation, it appears, is somewhat more important in cases of obesity than with any other problem. The compulsion to overeat is a powerful ego-satisfying drive. It isn't enough to rationalize intellectually that it is better for whatever reason. The rationalization must, or should be, of a deeply satisfying emotional nature, such as the feeling of triumph the woman experienced in thwarting her former boy friend. When the drive is strong, it is possible to reject sweets, because the image of herself at 125 pounds and with a new boy friend is usually powerful enough to carry over the first couple of weeks when that craving is strongest. After two weeks of abstinence, the craving usually subsides and the motivational drive takes over completely.

Chapter 21

How Jack Kicked His Acid Habit

MY OFFICE WAS darkened. The only light came from the faint illumination of a tiny night lamp in the outlet near the door. A young man with shaggy black hair was stretched out under a blanket that was drawn up to his whiskered chin. His eyes were closed tightly and he appeared to be in a deep sleep, lying horizontally in the professional, leather, reclining chair. Electrodes were attached to the occipital lobe of his head with another just above his right temple. His breathing was deep, almost labored. Actually he was enjoying a state of euphoria because the brain-wave analyzer attached to the electrodes was indicating alpha, with occasional bursts of theta, rhythms.

Jack had heard about NovaYoga and wanted to apply its teaching to help him overcome his hangups. He was a very apt subject. This was his fifth session and he had conditioned himself remarkably well. Now, he was able to reach deeply, with the aid of his imaginative faculty, into the very core of his subconscious. He was experiencing a delightful altered state of consciousness. He had been programmed, because of his many prior acid trips, to elicit psychedelic sensations and now, in the chair, without the use of any acid, he was on another delightful trip.

We had agreed on 15 minutes of altered consciousness, and now my voice in a yogic chant reached his ego, adrift in controlled reverie, through special stethoscopic earphones. "Concentrate now on the Yin/Yang . . . you will remember all your dream sensations as the seagull brings you back . . . back with the speed of thought . . . through the luminescent cloud with all the vibrating colors . . . back . . . back to your reality. . . ." My voice droned on softly, compellingly, authoritatively, bringing him back from his high.

In a few moments his eyes opened, staring at the ceiling, and then a bright smile spread over his face. He exclaimed, "Wow! That was the greatest! What an experience!" I adjusted the recliner to a sitting position and he sat there, breathing deeply, rubbing his hands to relieve the numbness. He broke out into a smile again as he began to speak. "I'll never risk taking acid again! Now that I know the procedure I've got it made!"

I smiled back at him but hastened to correct his impression. "You're an exceptional subject and I'm glad you've been able to experience this kind of altered state of consciousness. It generally takes a good deal of training; but remember Jack, my concern as your teacher is not to train you to controlled tripping but to help you overcome your hangups to enable you to mature emotionally."

"Yeah, yeah . . . I know. . . ." He still lingered on the edge of his euphoria, and then his expression changed abruptly as he asked, "Are you telling me that I shouldn't trip whenever I like?"

It was terribly important that he understood thoroughly the objectives of NovaYoga training. "I didn't say that. I told you when we began your training that your mind was like a computer. It was already programmed because of your previous acid trips. This programming is now stored within your memory bank and by training your imaginative faculty you can reexperience these sensations, exactly as you did just now."

I paused for possible questions and then added, "The really important fact that I want you to understand is that your prior use of hallucinogenic drugs – grass and acid – was prompted by a subliminal drive to repress anxieties, frustrations, tensions. All the 'trips' you've experienced were merely a means of escaping the tensions of your hangups."

He leaned back into the reclining chair, closed his eyes and appeared to muse for several moments. Then he spoke. "What you're telling me is that once I get over my hangups I'll have no need to trip, that right?"

To emphasize what I was going to say I leaned forward and poked my finger into his chest. "You are learning how to control the most powerful force in the world – your imaginative faculty! This is how Thomas Edison created his marvelous inventions despite the fact he had had no formal education. This is how Robert Louis Stevenson wrote his marvelous stories, telling his 'Brownies' to develop his ideas. This, I'm sure, is how Edgar Cayce was able to reach his trance state to release his imaginative faculty and his remarkable prophecies. This is how every creative person, whether he uses the NovaYoga technique or some method of his own, attains creative thought."

I paused again to allow him to accept what I had just said. But as he didn't question me, I continued: "The dynamics of the NovaYoga technique of self-realization lie within your imaginative faculty. This is the driving force that can make you ill through the development of your hangups. But this same power can make you well again by overcoming these self-same hangups. It's up to you to learn how to manipulate the power of your imaginative faculty, to enable you to become the person you want to be."

He was intelligent. He had an excellent imagination. He understood me. He nodded in approval, got up from the chair, slipped into his shoes and coat jacket, and asked for his next appointment.

When he left I began to study his record once more. I hadn't given any thought to employing the NovaYoga technique for anything other than its original purpose – to overcome hangups. Now, however, it appeared that the procedure would train the gifted subject to control his imaginative faculty in a manner that would enable him to reexperience psychedelic sensations.

The fact that Jack had been able to enter an altered state of consciousness and while there bring to his recall prior psychedelic sensations may have been impressive to him. But to me it was still another talented subject who was able to quickly learn how to control that awesome power that lies within his subconscious mind, that power that is released by means of the imaginative faculty.

Would this procedure be effective with persons more seriously addicted? I had been reluctant to experiment because of my limited facilities and total lack of clinical control. The only subject I accepted that would fit this category was an alcoholic referred to me by a clinical psychologist who thought suggestions and positive self-imagery implanted at the subconscious level could be helpful.

As it happened, this subject was in a spot. He wanted to overcome his alcoholism, yet he was in a business that called for him to entertain clients at lunches and dinners – where cocktails were the rule.

Contrary to the accepted principle – once an alcoholic, always an alcoholic – this man was conditioned (by means of subliminal imagery and suggestions) to the idea of one drink per occasion! This meant that lunch was an occasion, dinner was an occasion, a cocktail party was an occasion. He was conditioned to take one drink for each such occasion and no more! If he broke this rule he was conditioned to become sick!

The rationale, which he accepted, was based on the simple fact that alcohol was a stimulant in the limited quantity of one drink but a depressant in the larger quantities of more drinks. He accepted the image of himself (developing enormous self-esteem in the process) of taking one drink and enjoying it – and taking a second drink and becoming violently ill.

Following NovaYoga principles, this man was considered *matured* when he was able to report that he did become violently ill when he flaunted the rule.

A few days after my final session with Jack, I received the following letter:

> Dear Sir,
>
> On the basis of past experience I have found the NovaYoga technique to be superior to acid. I can completely direct my trip and not experience any negative side effects due to impure acid, poor environment or poor guidance.
>
> To anyone else who comes to you as I did I would suggest that he (or she) try your procedure and train himself to a "controlled trip."
>
> Yours sincerely,
> [name on file]

To which I hasten to add, while some young people may regard this kind of "controlled tripping" idyllic, the peace of mind that can be attained, the tranquility of spirit, the sheer joy of physical and mental well-being that proficiency in the NovaYoga technique of self-realization assures far outweighs any such transitory benefits.

Be the person you want to be!

An Invitation to the Reader

NOVAYOGA, THE YOGA of the imagination, can become the pathway of a whole new life for you. The NovaYoga technique of self-realization can bring you greater health, strength and tranquility, as you learn to control the awesome power that lies within your imaginative faculty.

NovaYoga can help you to function at your highest levels. You learn to release your innate talents, capabilities, and capacities. It can lead you to your happiness in fulfillment as you develop self-confidence, self-assurance, and self-esteem.

NovaYoga can lead you to your pearl of great price . . . *to be the person you want to be!*

You are invited to correspond with the author. The NovaYoga Center is seeking reports, either approving or disapproving, of persons who have studied and practiced the NovaYoga technique of self-realization. These reports will be held in strict confidence, but will be used in statistical evaluation of results obtained, with and without the use of cassette tapes.

It would be helpful if you explained your aspirations

and to what degree NovaYoga helped you to attain them. Your letter or your name will not be published without your permission. Address: The NovaYoga Center, Inc., Box 493, Cooper Union Station, New York, N.Y., 10003.

How to Eat and Grow Thin the NovaYoga Way

Eat and Grow Thin

If you consider the fact that your body is today little different from that of the caveman who was your ancestor, then perhaps you may be able to understand why certain foods keep you healthy while thin and other foods rob you of health while making you fat.

The caveman had no agriculture to give him grains, sugars, and the like. His diet consisted solely of proteins and fats. He had to be strong and healthy to survive the hostile environment. If he hadn't been healthy, you and I wouldn't be here discussing NovaYoga and nutrition now.

However, today, because of our extensive agriculture and the profitable processing of foods, we are offered a huge diversity of taste-tempting and alluring foods to beguile our appetities – while they rob us of the very elements of which our bodies are made!

Because of our unnatural and highly refined culture, most of us revert to a childhood pattern when we are emotionally motivated. We stuff ourselves with sweets and carbohydrates, foods that were given to us in abundance as children in the mistaken idea that their quick energy was good for us. All they did then was to make us chubby and cute. But now, following the same pattern, the same foods make us fat and ugly.

Obesity is an emotional problem. Simply put, you overeat in order to placate an ego-satisfying compulsion or you revert to an early conditioned pattern. The basic emotional problem is the hangup. It may be due to feelings of inferiority – feelings of inadequacy, feelings of insecurity, feelings of rejection, or it may stem from feelings of guilt. It has its roots in your early conditioning – insufficient love.

The NovaYoga procedure of weight control begins with the recognition that the basic problem is emotional – a hangup. You follow the same procedure as with any other emotional problem and you follow the sensible food intake regimen that is required. It is anti-hypoglycemic; that is, it will regulate your blood sugar and give you vim, vigor, and vitality!

The outstanding advantage of this procedure is that because you have overcome your basic hangup (in the procedure of losing weight), you will be able to maintain your normal weight forever.

Protein/Fat/Low Carbohydrate Food Intake Regimen

It is always a good idea to be checked annually by your doctor. If you are overweight he will advise you to lose some weight. You can ask him about this dietary regimen. He is familiar with it because it is an approved maintenance diet. It is not a spectacular quick-weight-loss diet. But if it becomes your regular food intake regimen, you will lose weight gradually and stay at your normal weight thereafter.

You will not feel hungry and you will not get that

gaunt look that crash dieters do. If you follow the complete procedure – NovaYoga exercises, breathing, meditation, *and* the diet – you will show improvement in as little as two weeks and continue to improve until you have reached the weight that is proper for your skeletal structure and energy requirements. Those who have followed this procedure report feeling stronger, more vigorous and energetic, happier, and looking better than they have in years.

MENU SUGGESTION (can be varied; see allowable foods)

ON ARISING: Drink a glass of unsweetened grapefruit juice.

BREAKFAST: Two eggs, any style, with two strips of bacon, crisped. No bread for the first two weeks, after which one slice of Thomas' Protogen Bread, toasted. Half a grapefruit or cantaloupe or any permitted fruit. *Decaffeinated* coffee with *no* sugar (if absolutely necessary use saccharin).

MIDMORNING (*or so-called coffee*) BREAK: A glass of milk or tomato juice.

LUNCH: Grapefruit juice; hamburger or chicken, one cooked (allowable) vegetable; cottage cheese salad with avocado (in season) or unsweetened pineapple; decaffeinated coffee, no sugar.

MIDAFTERNOON BREAK: Dry-roasted nuts or sunflower or pumpkin seeds.

DINNER: Grapefruit juice (always unsweetened); steak, tossed green salad with corn oil and apple vinegar; one cooked (allowable) vegetable; dietetic ice cream; decaffeinated coffee, no sugar.

BEDTIME SNACK: A glass of milk, or yogurt.

Drink water, up to six glasses a day. Take vitamins and minerals as supplements. A good vitamin and mineral formula, which you can find only in a health food store, is:

Vitamins (ingredients of two capsules)

Vitamin A (from fish liver oils) 7.5 mg	25,000 USP units
Vitamin D (from fish liver oils) 50 mcg	2,000 USP units
Thiamine (Vitamin B-1 from rice bran and yeast)	7 mg.
Riboflavin (Vitamin B-2 from rice bran and yeast	14 mg.
Ascorbic Acid (Vitamin C from Rose Hips and Acerola)	200 mg.
Niacin (from rice bran and yeast)	4.17 mg.
Cobalamin (Vitamin B-12 activity)	25 mcg.
Vitamin E (mixed tocopherols from vegetable oils)	50 Int. Units
Rutin (from Eucalyptus)	20 mg.
Lemon Bioflavonoid Complex	50 mg.
Nucleic Acid (from yeast)	20 mg.
Liver, desiccated and defatted	100 mg.
Papain (from Papaya)	60 mg.
Pepsin	60 mg.
Diatase of Malt	20 mg.
Hesperidin Complex (from citrus fruits)	10 mg.
l-Lysine (from fermentation extractives)	10 mg.
Wheat Germ	30 mg.
Pyridoxine (Vitamin B-6 from yeast concentrate)	0.35 mg.
Pantothenic Acid (from yeast concentrate)	0.63 mg.
Folic Acid (from yeast concentrate)	2.9 mcg.
Aminobenzoic Acid (from yeast concentrate)	2.1 mcg.
Choline (from yeast concentrate)	17.16 mg.
Inositol (from yeast concentrate)	7.75 mg.
Biotin (from yeast concentrate)	2.5 mcg.

Minerals (ingredients of two capsules)

Calcium (from bones of young cattle and dolomite)	375 mg.
Magnesium (from dolomite)	75 mg.
Phosphorus (from bones of young cattle)	97.5 mg.

Iron (from peptonized iron)	20 mg.
Iodine (from Pacific and Nova Scotia kelp)	0.1 mg.
Red Bone Marrow	20 mg.
Beef Peptone	40 mg.

Plus these minerals naturally occurring in the bones of young cattle: Copper, Manganese, and Potassium.

Your health food store man should be able to recognize this formula as being from one of the best, ethical producers of natural vitamins. The stress-reducing vitamins are in the B-complex area, and megavitamin therapy employs huge dosages of niacin, pyridoxine, pantothenic acid, with thiamine, riboflavin, ascorbic acid, with additions of biotin, inositol, and choline. The B vitamins are water soluble and are therefore safe to take in mega quantities because any excess, that which the body cannot utilize, is discarded in your urine. The vitamins obtained from oils should be taken in the suggested amounts only (although these amounts are far below tolerance) because they are retained in the body until they are completely used up.

A General Guide and the Best Protein Sources

This high-protein, moderate-fat, low-carbohydrate diet is easy to take because it eliminates the hunger tensions that usually cause one to want to nibble. The menu suggestion can be varied almost endlessly by changing the primary proteins in each meal. The best sources of protein are:

meat (not processed), chicken or game fowl, fish, shellfish, served approximately 1/4 lb. per meal

cheese and dairy products, eggs, bearing in mind that cream cheese and cottage cheese are approximately half the protein of other cheeses; avoid *processed* cheeses, buy only natural cheese, and to insure proper intestinal flora be sure to take plain yogurt frequently

nuts are also a good source of protein, especially butternuts, brazil nuts, pignolias, walnuts, pecans, and seeds such as sunflower and pumpkin

Remember, there is no dietary regimen that allows you to overeat. And the cause of obesity is obviously overeating. This is why most dieters eventually swing back and regain their weight on a kind of yo-yo cycle. And it is why regulating your weight by means of NovaYoga is truly successful because you overcome the casual factor, the basic hangup, which motivates your subconscious craving for food. If you bought this book in order to learn how to control your weight, be of good cheer; all you have to do is to apply yourself to the study and application of all the exercises, mental and physical, overcome your hangups resulting from your early traumatic experiences, and you've got it made! Once you have recognized your causal factor, rationalized the emotional response, you will become mature in your control of your subconscious motivations. Your new self-image and your new self-esteem will keep you at your proper and most healthful weight.

FOODS TO AVOID

alcoholic drinks
barley
beans, dried
blueberries
bread
caffeine
candy
canned fruits
canned meats
caramel
cashews
cereals
chestnuts
chewing gum
chocolate
cocoa
coffee
cola drinks
cold cuts
cookies
corn and corn products
crackers
custards
dessert toppings
dextrose
dried beans
dried peas
dried fruits
fructose

glucose
grape juice
grapes
grits
guava
hominy
honey
hot dogs
huckleberries
jams
jelly
Jell-O
lactose
lima beans
macaroni
malt
maltose
mango
manitol
marmalade
matzoh
matzoh meal
molasses
noodles
Ovaltine
pancakes
papaya juice
pastry
pickles, sweet
pie
pizza
plantain
postum
potato chips
potatoes
pretzels
prune juice
puddings
relishes, sweet
rice
rolls
salami
sausages
scrapple
shell beans, lima and others
soft drinks
Sorbitol
spaghetti
sucrose
sugar of any kind
sweet potatoes, yams
sweet relishes
syrup
tea, strong
waffles

ALLOWABLE FOODS (those marked with an asterisk are to be eaten very sparingly) (% of carbohydrate)

apples* – 15%
apricots* – 15%
apricot juice* – 15%
artichoke – 15%
asparagus – 6%
avocado – 7%
bamboo shoots – 6%
beans, green wax – 10%
bean sprouts – 6%
beets – 15%
blackberries* – 15%
blackberry juice* – 15%
boysenberries* – 10%
Broccoli – 6%
broth, clear
Brazil nuts
brussels sprouts – 10%
butter
butternuts
cabbage, raw – 6% – cooked – 10%
cantaloupe – 10%
carrots – 10%
casaba melon – 10%
cauliflower – 6%
celery – 3%
chard – 6%
cheese, not processed
cherries* – 15%
chervil – 10%
chicory – 3%
Chinese cabbage – 3%
chives – 3%
coconut – 10%

coffee, decaffeinated
collard greens – 10%
cottage cheese
cranberries, raw – 10%
cucumbers – 3%
dairy products
dandelion greens – 6%
egg plant – 6%
eggs
elderberries* – – 10%
endive – 3%
escarole – 3%
fennel – 3%
fish
fowl
fruit salad, fresh – no grapes* – 10%
gooseberries* – 10%
grapefruit – 15%
grapefruit juice – 15%
herb teas
honeydew melon* – 10%
kale – 6%
kohlrabi – 10%
leeks – 6%
lemons – 10%
lemon juice – 10%
lettuce – 3%
limes, – 10%
loganberries* – 15%
meat, all kinds
melons* – 10%
milk
mushrooms – 6%
mustard greens – 6%
nuts, dry roasted
oils, cold pressed
okra – 6%
olives – 3%
onions – 10%
orange juice* – 15%
parsley – 3%
parsnips – 15%
peaches* – 15%
pears – 15%
peas – 6%
pea pods
pecan nuts
peppers, green – 6%
pickles, dill – 3%
pignolias
pimentos – 6%
pineapple, fresh*
pumpkin* – 15%
pumpkin seeds
radishes – 3%
raspberries* – 15%
rhubarb* – raw 3% – cooked – 6%
rutabaga – 10%
salad oil
Sanka coffee
sauerkraut – 6%
shellfish
soybeans – 15%
spinach – 6%
squash* summer – 6% – winter – 15%
tangerines* – 15%
tea, weak*
tomatoes – 6%
tomato juice – 6%
turnips –6%
turnip greens – 6%
walnuts
water chestnuts
watercress – 3%
yogurt, plain
zucchini – 6%

You should avoid *all* carbohydrates – sugar and starch – especially wheat and cereal products.

The NovaYoga Weekend Vegefast

As Dr. Bieler points out in his book, *Food Is Your Best Medicine*, overweight is compounded by a state of toxemia. Your liver and probably your kidneys are terribly overworked and are just limping along because they are probably plugged with toxic substances. He has had considerable success with vegetable juices in neutralizing acidity in the body. For this reason it is recommended that you obtain a juicer and prepare for a weekend vegetable fast.

Here's how it works: supply yourself with celery, carrots, a few apples, zucchini, and beets. An excellent formula for neutralizing toxic acids is two stalks of celery, one carrot, one small zucchini, ½ beet, and ½ apple. Dilute the juice with about ¼ distilled water (or buy bottled water). Don't mind the color, because it will look muddy. With the addition of the apple it will be delicious.

This much juice diluted with the water could last you through the morning of your first day's vegefast. The juice is best if it is prepared fresh. However, if you do not own or do not wish to invest in a juicer, you can get your local health food store to prepare it for you. Go prepared with several quart containers that have tight closures. Have the containers filled to the very top before sealing, to eliminate all trapped air.

When you begin this NovaYoga weight control regimen with this vegefast, on Saturday through Sunday, you will find that you will have hunger pangs only up to Saturday lunch. After that the vegetable juice can be taken as often as you wish. At first you'll be sipping frequently, but soon you'll shift into your normal routine or lunchtime and dinnertime.

The following Monday will see you on the regimen

– grapefruit juice, protein, some fat, no (or extremely little) carbohydrates. On this basis you will lose on the average two or to four pounds each week until you have reached your target weight, when you will be able to loosen up just a little on the restrictions on carbohydrates – but only a little. You should find yourself feeling wonderful, especially if you have also continued with the exercises, breathing, and meditation. Improved blood circulation, with increased oxygen intake, now combined with a blood-sugar-regulating food intake regimen, will have you more alert, more energetic, more full-of-life than you've felt in years.

The Best Snack Food You Can Eat

The more you investigate nutrition the more you marvel at the bounties nature has prepared for us – bounties in health-giving vitamins and minerals which our modern food processors blithely eliminate to serve us foodstuffs that are virtually dead – all because of shelf life. Yes, only because good, wholesome, vitamin-rich food spoils quickly, you are served bread that is no better than library paste, cheese that has been "processed" so it is no better than a lump of starch. When someone raises his voice in protest he is called a food faddist or worse, a health-food nut.

Well, you're going to become a health-food nut! Because it's going to give a sparkle to your life you could never get with the lifeless pap you are being sold in packages in your supermarket. Let's start with that delicious, nutty morsel that is the finest snack food you can imagine. It possesses the seed of life, a storehouse of all the elements you need to promote your feeling of well-being.

It is a remarkable source of Vitamin F, so hard to get

in our "processed" diets since all oils are "refined" today. This is linoleic acid, an essential fatty acid which helps prevent harmful deposits of cholesterol and helps provide a beautiful skin and healthy hair. It is especially rich in Vitamin E, as much as 31 units in every 3½ ounces, essential to the health of your reproductive processes, for your heart and muscle health and a preventative of blood clots. It contains more of the B-complex (thiamine, riboflavin, niacin) than an equivalent quantity of wheat germ – great for the nail-biting jitters.

This wonder food has as much as 50 units of Vitamin A in every 100 grams! Vitamin D, one of the most difficult to obtain, is amply supplied! Then there's zinc, vital to the sex glands of men; magnesium, essential to the formation of strong blood vessels and nerves that can take it; pectin, which has a beneficial effect on the level of blood cholestrol; protein, high in methinonine, an amino acid usually lacking in vegetable foods, as well as the 10 essential amino acids not found in nutritious amounts except in meat and fish; minerals, an excellent source of essential minerals, and finally enzymes, vital to life itself.

What is this giant wonder food? Tasty, nutty, delicious, sunflower seeds.

Eat them on your new food-intake regimen as your snack-food, while watching TV, at midmorning and mid-afternoon breaks. You'll love 'em. Facing the sun, as they do all day, every day, they absorb the life force which they bring to you *unprocessed.*

And Finally—the Sprouts

Metabolism, the process by which the body's fuel is converted into energy, relies heavily on enzymes, which are specialized protein molecules that act as catalysts in aiding bodily processes. One of the finest sources of enzymes is sprouts.

Vitamin-rich, mineral-rich, enzyme-rich sprouts are the most spectacular food you eat while the vibrant life force is at its highest potential. Everything that has been said about sunflower seeds can be said again about sprouts! And they are the easiest, quickest and least expensive source of your primary nutriment. Here's how:

Your health food store has organically grown seeds, sesame, millet, clover, parsley, mustard, fenugreek, lentils, soybeans, mung beans, alfalfa, and more. Start with a combination of alfalfa, mung beans, and lentils (this is a packaged combination already mixed put up by Siloh). Take a small tea strainer and pour some of the seeds into it, about a quarter inch deep. Place this in a small bowl and pour water into the bowl until it just covers the seeds. Place a small saucer on the bowl to exclude light and place this bowl into a warm, dark place (such as the oven of your stove), but don't turn on the heat.

Next morning, take out the bowl, pour off any water that remains, fill the bowl with the seeds (which have now tripled in volume). Then add water to rinse the seeds, turning the bowl over while holding the seeds back with a splatter shield (or with your hand). When the seeds are rinsed and moist, replace the saucer and replace the covered bowl in the oven. Repeat the process again the following morning. However, now you will find the volume has increased again and there will be sprouts showing. The third day should do it; the sprouts will be one to three inches long and ready to eat.

You can prepare them in many ways. Use them for your midmorning and midafternoon snacks with yogurt – great! Use a handful with a couple of eggs to make an omelet. You can mix your bacon in with them to give your omelet a taste supreme. Or add them to soups, hamburgers, or sandwiches instead of lettuce, and certainly to your tossed salads. Keep them in covered jars in your refrigerator; cooked or raw, they'll give you a vitamin mineral enzyme health boost.

ACKNOWLEDGMENTS

I wish to express my deep appreciation to the many researchers, teachers and writers, whose works have supplied answers to my questing, particularly: Joseph Oliver DiVincent, who guided my earliest meditations seeking to know the Absolute; Dr. William J. Bryan, Jr., who later taught me the art of counseling and hypnotherapy; Dr. Attilio Morpurgo, whose approval of my original thesis How to Be the Person You Want to Be! *inspired me to expand it to its present form.*

I want to thank also a student of NovaYoga, and a doctoral student of Eastern religious philosophies, Shakti Tarsy, for her graceful interpretations of the hathayoga exercises pictured in this book.

G.F.B.